D0518643

FICTION

COVER PICTURE: CAMERA PRESS

FEATURES

FANCY THAT!

TEATIME TREATS

BRAIN BOOSTERS

DC Thomson

Queens Of Cakes!

Meet the kitchen superstars who've kept us entertained and informed over the years…

Having started her career more years ago than there are currants in a Bath bun, Mary has brought baking full circle with her traditional skills now shown in the modern setting of *TheGreat British Bake Off.*

2010s

Lorraine Pascale

Retraining as a chef after a successful modelling career, Lorraine has displayed a deft skill in the kitchen, making absolutely delicious dishes that aspiring chefs can imitate. A model baker!

2000s

More Overleaf

1990s

Nigella Lawson

Her first cookery book, *How To Eat,* reminded us of the sensual pleasures of food, and Nigella is known for her selfless devotion to making sure we enjoy the luxuries of eating! A nation of men rejoice.

1980s

Jane Asher

The lady baker who started the whole cake craze! Her wonderful creations and use of coloured fondant icing started a phenomenon which is still going strong today. Pass the cupcakes, darling!

More Overleaf

1970s

Delia Smith

Look out for "the Delia Effect" – so trusted is this TV chef, if Delia recommends a culinary ingredient, it will fly off supermarket shelves in the next few days. A baker with nerves of steel!

1960s

Fanny Cradock

The nation's first ever TV chef – bringing luxury and exotica to the aspiring housewife – cooking in a ballgown without a pinny, and bullying Johnnie, her long-suffering screen husband.

Janey Fraser

The Girl In The Blue Bonnet

It wasn't just a love of books that had been passed down through the family, as Gillian was to find out...

Eliza turned the wafer thin pages carefully, marvelling at the illustrations. Such stars! And just look at the moon. The way that it was peeping out of the cloud was truly magical. Even the delicate pen and ink folds on the heroine's dress were carefully drawn with the precision that only a talented artist could accomplish, surely. Oh, how she would love to own such a book as this!

"What are you doing, child?" demanded her mother sharply, sweeping towards her in a rustle of stern satin. "We are here to purchase an atlas for your brother; not to indulge ourselves in books that fill our head with nonsense."

She cast a disapproving look at the dark green tome which Eliza quickly closed before she could be reproved further.

Mama – or Mrs Marchmont as the shopkeepers referred to her – was not known for her sentimentality. That side, the "sensitive side" as her mother would say bitingly, had come from her dear father who was long dead.

Eliza could scarcely remember Papa but she did have a hazy memory of a kindly man with vivid blue eyes, just like her own, reading to her from a wonderful book such as this. It was full of tales of witches and heroines and dashing knights on white horses.

If Eliza closed her eyes, she could recall her father's warm voice as he led her through almost certain pitfalls which then resulted in good overcoming bad.

"Where did father's books go?" she once asked when she had wrongly judged Mama to be in a good mood.

Immediately, she had realised from the furrowed brow and sharp tone, that she had asked the wrong question.

"Where do you think? They had to be sold, did they not, in order for us to have something to live on."

Now however, a few years on, life was becoming more comfortable. Thomas her brother, was to go away to school which was why he required an atlas. Their guardian, Walter Gentlehorn, a

If Eliza closed her eyes, she could recall her father's wonderful, warm voice

Continued overleaf...

ILLUSTRATIONS: THINKSTOCK, MANDY DIXON

How she would love to own a book like this

Continued from previous page

friend of their father's with a thin pinched nose and spectacles which made her feel as though he could see right inside her, was to "foot the bill" as her mother put it. In return, 16-year-old Eliza had accepted his hand in marriage.

"We owe it to Walter," her mother declared in case there was any doubt. "He has been very good to us since your father's passing."

The marriage was to take place the following Friday; a date which seemed quite unreal in Eliza's mind.

Every time she looked at Walter with his thin nose and glasses, she felt a shiver running down her. It was not a shiver such as those described by the heroines in the books which she borrowed secretly from friends at the sewing circle. No. It was taken them to the opera at Christmas.

"You like fairy tales?" asked the young man. He had warm brown eyes, Eliza noticed, which weren't obscured by glasses and his lips were full, unlike Walter's which were so narrow that the top part seemed to retreat completely into the space below his nose.

She nodded, casting a quick look at Mama who was deep in conversation with her brother over the advantages of one atlas over another.

"I do indeed, although I fear that I am too old for them now, especially as I am to be married."

Eliza said the last bit in a rush, partly to protect herself in case this young man should think she was being too forward in engaging in such conversation.

She felt his hand touch her arm briefly and it was all she could do not to cry out

a shiver of foreboding; a dark feeling of dread mixed at the same time with the knowledge that she had to perform her duty.

"It is a beautiful book, is it not?" asked a voice behind her.

Eliza gave a little start and pretended to adjust her blue bonnet out of nervousness. Fortunately, Mama was busy at the far corner of a shop, perusing yet another atlas. Otherwise she would not have taken kindly to a stranger addressing her in such an intimate fashion.

"It is enchanting," she replied, unable to help herself. Her slim index finger reached out to trace the outlines of the moon which was hidden behind a sheet of crispy transparent paper. Each one of the illustrations was protected in this way. It was like a curtain, Eliza thought; such as the one on stage when Walter had

"Nonsense," he declared, stepping back. "No-one is ever too old for fairy tales especially when they look like a fairy princess themselves."

It took a second for Eliza to realise that the young man was referring to her.

Taking a step backwards, she almost tripped over the lace of her boot which had become undone. As she did so, she felt his hand touch her arm briefly. It was all she could do not to cry out with the heat that seared through her body.

At that very moment, the door opened with the sound of a little bell and, to her dismay, Eliza saw Walter, peering at her through his glasses as though he knew she had done something wrong.

"Ah, there you are, my dear." He stumbled towards her, on his stick, and took her arm; the same one that the

young man had touched briefly. But instead of heat, Eliza now felt a coolness that made her forehead clammy and set a pain racing through her temples.

"Mr Gentlehorn," enthused her mother excitedly as she bustled her way through the shop to greet him. "How very good of you to meet us here. I believe we have found exactly the atlas we require."

Eliza's betrothed touched his hat. "I am glad to hear that." Then he turned to the young man with warm brown eyes.

"Would you be so good as to wrap it up and send it to the following address?" He placed a card on the desk before turning to Eliza, Thomas and their mother. "Shall we go? My carriage is outside, waiting."

Do not look back, Eliza told herself as she followed her brother to the door. She almost made it but, just at the point when she was about to place her foot on the carriage with the aid of Mr Gentlehorn's firm grip, she glanced at the window.

There, surrounded by a display of books, was the young man with the brown eyes; staring at her just like the knight in the fairy tales as though they were all characters in a story, bound together by hope and disaster and a bottle green cover.

How silly you are, Eliza, she told herself. *Mama is right. Your imagination will do you no good whatsoever.*

Continued overleaf...

Continued from previous page

The following Friday, on the morning of her wedding, a parcel was delivered, with Eliza's own name on the outside. Fortunately, Mama was still dressing so Eliza was able to open it, undisturbed. Her heart beat fast as she unwrapped the brown paper and withdrew a tome with a green cover and gold writing on the front. Her fairy tale book!

Inside was an inscription in bold hand and black ink: *To the princess with the blue bonnet, on her wedding day. July 12, 1902.*

What do you think it means?" asked Gillian as she breathed in the curiously addictive musty smell. "I know there are lots of books with great aunt Eliza's name in them – don't you love the way that people wrote an inscription in those days? But this one is so romantic! The princess with the blue bonnet on her wedding day. How lovely!"

Her sister snorted. "Romantic? In those days, people got married for convenience and frankly, I don't blame them. Look where love has got us!"

It was true. Neither Gillian nor her sister Marion had been lucky "in that department" as her mother often put it. Two failed marriages (Marion) and one long term relationship which

"It's so romantic," sighed Gillian

seemed to be going nowhere (Gillian) wasn't what their mother had in mind. Sometimes, Gillian thought her mother fancied herself as a Mrs Bennet from *Pride and Prejudice*: desperate to marry off her daughters even though, in today's day and age, marriage really wasn't necessary. Even so, Gillian did wish that Martin would pop the question before too long.

"Eliza's husband must have given it to her on their wedding day," mused Gillian, leafing through the book's thin pages, tenderly. "These illustrations are really beautiful. Look at this moon! Such exquisite detail – the folds of that dress are incredible."

In another life, Gillian would have loved to have been an artist. Instead she had to make do with watercolour classes one evening a week and a full-time job at customer relations for a big department store in town.

Her sister, who'd always been good at geography and maths, worked as an accountant for a company that made atlases.

"Probably worth a bit," sniffed Marion, glancing at the bottle green cover. "Why don't you take it into the auction house during one of your lunch breaks? You have more time than I do."

Her sister was always inferring that she worked harder than anyone else. Still, Gillian didn't mind. She often browsed around the auction rooms in town when she had a chance; there was something about old things that held her spellbound, pulled her back into another world where life was simpler and rules were clearer.

Besides, she thought, looking around great aunt Eliza's little cottage wistfully, there were some other bits and pieces that would need to go to auction.

Martin wouldn't care for them in the modern apartment he owned and which she had moved into, nearly three years ago. And her mother, a happily independent widow who was currently on yet another cruise, certainly didn't have room for anything else.

Gillian thought her mother fancied herself as Mrs Bennet from *Pride and Prejudice*

The following morning, it happened to be surprisingly quiet at work, allowing Gillian to slip off to the auction room just before the lunchtime rush. Under her arm, she carried the green book of fairy tales which she had been unable to put down ever since she'd found it.

The auction room was housed in a nondescript greyish building but as soon as one went in, it was like entering an Aladdin's cave.

"An old chest of drawers or a chipped china vase might seem like junk, but remember that someone once loved it," her father used to say.

The thought of her father always brought a big lump to Gillian's throat. He had been a furniture restorer in his spare time and was always taking her to auctions or sales.

"Do you see this?" he had said once, pointing to an intricately carved bookcase with a wobbly shelf. "We can fix that in no time." So he bought it for almost nothing and the bookcase now sat

Continued overleaf...

Continued from previous page

by her side of the bed, even though Martin complained that it "didn't go" with his modern oak furniture.

"May I help you?" asked a voice. Gillian started. Usually, the man who sat behind the auction office door was an older gentleman with a bald head and a jolly, ruddy complexion. Today, there was a younger man – about her age – with the same ruddy complexion and warm brown eyes.

"Actually, I've come to ask if you would do a house clearance for us. That is, my sister and I." She felt her words coming out awkwardly, even though the nature of her customer services job meant she was used to talking to strangers.

His eyes dropped down to the book below her arm.

"I also wondered if you could tell me anything about this," she added. "It's not for sale but I'm intrigued by it."

Carefully, in a way that suggested a certain reverence, he took the book, carefully turning the thin pages.

"Fairy tales," he declared enthusiastically. "My daughter loves them! What beautiful pictures." Then he shook his head. "Pity about the inscription."

"Why?"

"It devalues the book. First edition too." He let out a little whistle. "I don't know any more about it but I could look it up if you want and get back to you."

He handed it back to her and as he did so, their hands brushed and an unexpected burning sensation shot through Gillian's body.

"Would you liked to give me your number and we can arrange that house clearance at the same time?"

He's married, Gillian told herself. And she had rules about that sort of thing, even if it was old-fashioned nowadays.

"I'll think about it," she said. And then, in case he thought she was being rude, she added, "Thank you."

By the time their mother came back from her cruise, it was sorted.

"We got quite a lot of money from all that bric-a-brac," announced her sister proudly as though it was she who had done the running around instead of Gillian. "Could have got more if someone here hadn't insisted on hanging on to all those books."

Her mother, who was sporting a tan and yet another engagement ring, shook her head. "Just like your father. Sometimes, dear, you have to let go of the past."

"You're just like your father. Sometimes, dear, you have to let go of the past"

Gillian took a deep breath. "Actually, I have. Martin and I have split up."

Her mother's face crumpled. "Now you're really going to be left on the shelf."

"Mum!" Even Marion looked shocked. "Nowadays, lots of people choose to be on their own."

But her mother wasn't listening.

"Well, I blame your father's side of the family. It all started with your great aunt Eliza."

Gillian stiffened. "What do you mean?"

"Didn't you know? She ran off with someone on the morning of her wedding day. A shopkeeper, can you believe! Her family disinherited her of course, but she was totally unrepentant. Your father always said he loved visiting their bookshop by the sea."

By now, Gillian could hardly breathe.

A bookshop by the sea. Of course! Why had she never thought of that before. She couldn't wait to tell Matt.

Elizabeth was enchanted by the book

"Did the knight marry the princess and live happily ever after?" asked Elizabeth, her eyes wide open as Gillian reached the last page.

She nodded. "Definitely." At that age, as she knew all too well, it was so important to have a happy ending.

When Matt had come round for the house clearance and explained that he was only filling in for his uncle – and that he actually lived thirty miles away, on the coast, near his ex-wife and daughter Elizabeth – she had felt a lightness in her heart. And when they had dinner (at his suggestion) to discuss their joint love of books and art, that little voice inside her head grew more and more insistent.

Of course, she felt terrible about telling Martin, who, somewhat surprisingly, immediately asked her to marry him.

"I'm sorry," she tried to explain gently, "but I don't think we were ever right for each other."

"When the princess gets married," asked Elizabeth, her little voice bringing her back to the present, "will she wear a blue hat?"

Gillian felt a tingle down the back of her spine. She hadn't read the inscription to the child; only the stories.

"Why?" she asked gently.

Elizabeth yawned. "I just think it would be nice if she did. You could wear one too."

"Then we will," declared Gillian, reaching out for Matt's hand.

She'd intended to go hatless but maybe there would just be time to buy one before next Friday when they made their oaths. A blue hat to match her eyes! A floppy one with flowers perhaps. Somehow, she couldn't help thinking that the book – and great aunt Eliza – would rather like that.

Turn the page for more from Janey...

Janey's Journey

Do you think you have what it takes to be a writer? Then let novelist Janey Fraser's advice inspire you…

You write under many different personas – is it fun to have different styles of writing?

It can be fun, actually! I was quite surprised to discover that I have different writing voices. It certainly stops me from getting bored with just one. I also find that one voice can help another. For instance, my historical persona might suddenly think of something that might help my contemporary romances.

Where do you like to write?

At the top of our house in my study which overlooks the sea. I have a sofa bed behind me, which our dog sleeps on. He usually prods me after 2000 words and then we go for a walk along the beach. That's my thinking time.

Which character is your own favourite creation?

In *The Blue Bonnet*, it's definitely Eliza. She believes in love and she loves books just like me! In my latest book *Happy Families*, it's a toss up between Bobbie and Vanessa. Everyone thinks that Bobbie is me (harassed mother) but I have a soft spot for Vanessa who's a glamorous young gran, running a second-hand designer shop. Just as she finds true love, her long-lost granddaughter turns up on the doorstep and her priorities change overnight.

What is your inspiration?

Crazy things that happen to me. My children, my husband, my friends. The sea… life… memories. Not necessarily in that order.

What do you like to read?

Anything that has believable characters and a plot that works, without any holes. It's frustrating to get to the end and think "That couldn't have happened" or "She wouldn't think like that". But I also want to slip into a different world so there has to be a degree of suspended belief.

Do you have afavourite author?

I have a bunch! Maggie O'Farrell. Rachel Joyce. Fay Weldon. Anne Tyler. Edna O'Brien. Rose Tremain.

How do you manage your time?

I like to write early in the day and then do emails in the afternoon. Then I have a second burst in the evening. Recently, I've tried to stop working by about seven but it doesn't always happen because there are always emails! They're a mixed blessing. Now my children are older, I'm not rushing around so much, but when they are around, I cancel anything I've

Janey Fraser

organised to be with them. They have to come first. When they were little and I was a journalist, I would take them with me to interviews if possible.

How do you relax?

Don't laugh – belly dancing! Also tennis, cycling, watching films with my husband, walking the dog, being with friends.

What is your best advice to a budding writer?

Write about something you feel passionate about. Make yourself write something every day, even if it's only a few words – you can always go back to it. Make sure something big happens in each chapter. Create warm characters with problems that the reader wants them to solve. Make the dialogue *say* something so that it adds to the plot. Finish it, even if you have doubts, because then you will have self-respect. Revise, revise, revise. Go to literary festivals and get advice from publishers and agents.

What did you do when you got your first acceptance letter?

It was a phone call from my agent, actually. I couldn't believe it – especially as it came at a very difficult time in my personal life. It didn't seem real. I also thought, "Yes! Someone believes in me at last."

JANEY'S LATEST BOOK

After The Honeymoon
Two couples, one romantic honeymoon destination, and enough secrets to bring both marriages to an end! Don't miss Janey's latest roller-coaster novel!
And find stories by your favourite authors in My Weekly every week

Christmas Stocking Emergency

When things don't go to plan, Ben's grandparents have to think quickly to recreate the magical day he was expecting

By Linda Gruchy

Tricia sank into the armchair with a satisfied sigh.

"Everything's ready for the morning, I've even wrapped the turkey for the oven. I do love a proper family Christmas dinner. I'm so looking forward to our Emma, James and little Ben coming over."

She gazed round the living room with satisfaction. The tree, fresh and pine scented, nearly touched the ceiling, thick with branches and bejewelled with baubles. The fairy lights winked and twinkled, making the tinsel glisten. The mantelpiece was swathed in cotton wool, with a nativity scene laid out, while red-berried holly gleamed from every corner.

"I might be a grandma now, but I still think Christmas is wonderful and I don't think I will ever outgrow that magic."

John smiled as he poured the coffee. "Do you want something extra in this? It is Christmas Eve after all."

"No thanks, or I'll be asleep in the armchair, and it's only just gone nine."

John gave her a saucy smile. "I think we should stand under the mistletoe…"

The strident ringing of the doorbell interrupted him. It was so persistent and unnerving they exchanged looks of alarm. John went to answer the door.

"I might be a grandma now, but I don't think I will every outgrow that magic"

"Thank goodness. I thought you might be out at a carol service," said their son-in-law James, standing on the doorstep with their four-year-old grandson Ben wrapped up in pyjamas and coat. "I tried phoning but you were engaged. The baby's coming. Fast."

"But she's not due for another three

Continued overleaf…

Ben couldn't wait for Father Christmas to arrive

Continued from previous page
weeks," gasped Tricia, rushing out to the car where her daughter Emma was sitting, wan faced, groaning quietly as another contraction hit her.

"Try telling the baby that," retorted James.

Emma wound the window down. "Sorry to spring this on you, Mum, but the contractions started suddenly and they're every three minutes. Nothing, then suddenly, woomf. We have to hurry." Her face took on a focused look. "Not another… I've only just. Ooooh."

James pecked Tricia on the cheek. "Bye Mum, gotta dash. Be good, Ben." James scrambled back into the car and drove off as fast as care would allow.

Tricia stood still, listening to the retreating car engine cleaving the silence of the night, before shaking herself and going back inside.

Ben was blinking and owl-eyed in the hall. John removed Ben's coat. "Best get you back to bed, young man."

Ben allowed his grandad to usher him towards the stairs, but caught sight of the Christmas tree in the living room and howled, "I left my Christmas stocking at home. Now Father Christmas won't be able to fill it."

"Don't worry," said John. "I expect Father Christmas will find it anyway, even though you're not there."

"No he won't. And I've been a good boy. I don't like the baby for coming on Christmas Eve. That's very bad manners."

Tricia nearly laughed because she could hear Emma's voice in that last remark, but little Ben looked so forlorn, she hadn't the heart to.

John went down on one knee to speak to Ben face to face. "Now don't be silly Ben. It's not the baby's fault, and you mustn't be cross with her. Babies just come when they have to, and there's nothing we can do about it. I know; let's hang up one of my walking socks instead."

"Babies come when they have to," explained Ben's grandad

Ben followed John upstairs to the spare bedroom. He looked unconvinced as John offered him a long walking sock.

"But that's not the same, Grandad. Mine has a picture of a rocking horse and shiny bits on it, specially for Christmas. And there's no way to hang this one up." The tears started trickling down his upturned face.

Tricia gave him a hug. "Don't cry, love, I'm sure Father Christmas won't mind what sort of stocking you hang up."

"When I was a little boy we never had special Christmas stockings," said John. "I used to use a stocking just like this, one of my dad's and it got filled up just the same. Now you get into bed and dry your eyes, and I'll get some string and show you what I used to do."

Ben climbed into bed.

John made a loop of string and pegged it to the sock. "Hang it up then, Ben, and I'll read you a bedtime story."

Ben hung the sock on one of the bed knobs, and studied it dubiously.

"Lie back," said Tricia, sitting on the bed.

Ben did as he was bidden, and Tricia gently stroked his forehead as John read him the Christmas Story. Ben's eyes drooped, then closed, a quiet smile on his lips. He was asleep.

Downstairs in the living room, as John and Tricia sat down again, John chuckled. "I'm not sure I approve of fancy stockings for Christmas. Detracts from the majesty, makes it tawdry and commercialised. I used to love feeling the filled stocking in the dark, all knobbly with exciting potential, and trying to guess what was in it."

"A half a crown, an orange, some sweets, a couple of satsumas, an apple, some nuts, a chocolate Santa, and a couple of toys."

John laughed again. "How did you know?"

"Mine was the same. But kids nowadays expect more in their stockings." Tricia put her hands to her face as the blood drained to her toes. "Eeek... it's all very well hanging one of your walking socks up, but what on Earth are we going to put in the stocking? Ben's stocking presents will be at their house. I fear Father Christmas is a little unprepared."

John's face fell. "Oops. I'll drive over and see if I can find what they were going to use, maybe even find Ben's fancy stocking."

"No you will not! We had a sherry before supper, and wine with it. There's no way either of us is fit to drive. And besides, we don't yet have a key to their new front door. We'll just have to see what we can find here."

"I expect we have some sweets in the cupboard, but what about toys? It's not as if we can pinch a little present from under the tree."

They had bought Ben a go-kart, hidden away, swathed in an acre of wrapping paper; one big present rather than lots of small ones this year.

"You sort out the sweeties etc and I'll go on a hunt for odds and ends," suggested Tricia.

"Don't cry, I'm sure Father Christmas won't mind what stocking you hang up"

Upstairs, in one of her drawers, Tricia kept a little cache of felt tip pens and other sundries. Ben had a habit of leaving the lids off so she usually had a new set put by. She was delighted to find not only some felt tip pens, but a pencil case she'd bought in the post Back-to-School sales and forgotten about.

While rummaging, she came across one of her "lavender bunnies"; ancient, home-made rabbits made of felt and stuffed with lavender to keep her clothes fresh.

She held one to her nose and sniffed, shutting her eyes and remembering Christmases when she was a child and money was short. There had been a lavender bunny in her Christmas stocking

Continued overleaf...

Continued from previous page

every year, until she'd caught her mother making one and the secret was out.

When their daughter Emma was a child, Tricia, carrying on her mother's tradition, made a bunny or two for Emma's Christmas stockings, but this had petered out in the face of competition from more fashionable, glitzy stocking-fillers.

I wonder if Emma remembers, she mused to herself.

They were very simple to make, really; two pieces of felt overstitched together, then stuffed with lavender, with French knots for eyes, embroidered mouth, and ears sewn on separately. The whiskers were made of fine fishing line.

All Tricia's little lavender bunnies were very "loved", ancient and too scruffy to give as a gift, but she thought she had some felt squares in her sewing box, and possibly even the pattern.

A little later John found her in the kitchen, sitting at the table, needle and thread busy. She had sewn one rabbit already, filled with stuffing pilfered from a new pillow she'd been keeping by, and was busy with another in a different coloured felt.

"Clever old you," he said, giving her a hug. "I'd forgotten all about those cute little things. That's given me a thought..."

He disappeared off into the garage, reappearing half an hour later with a smug look. Another rabbit had joined the first. "Oh, look, they're breeding like..."

"I wonder if I can make an elephant in the same way," pondered Tricia turning over a grey square of felt. "Or maybe a mouse. What were you up to out there?"

"Making something," said John airily.

"What exactly?"

"Something with my fretsaw."

"Hmm, was that entirely wise, operating a machine after a couple of glasses of wine? If we're not fit to drive, you're not fit to operate a power tool."

"Count my fingers," said John defiantly. "And watch you don't prick yourself since you're drunk in charge of a needle."

"John Arnold Harris, I am not drunk... and you are incorrigible!"

Four hours later, way past midnight, and there was a menagerie on the kitchen table; two rabbits, an elephant, a rather soppy looking lion with a woolly mane, a hedgehog made of a scrap of fur fabric, and a bright red ladybird.

The phone went, freezing her heart. It was James calling from the hospital

"My fingers are aching," complained Tricia. A sudden qualm hit her. She was chuffed with her efforts but supposing Ben was disappointed? Children were so sophisticated nowadays. Perhaps home-made stuffed toys weren't good enough.

John slipped off into the garage, returning with a yellow fretwork sign saying "Ben".

"Thank goodness for quick drying spray paint," he said. "Look. It stands up."

"Oh, that's lovely. No word from the hospital, though..." Tricia bit her lip.

"Perhaps they've had the baby, but decided only complete lunatics would be awake at two am in the morning. Happy Christmas, love."

He gathered her into his arms, the way

Soon Tricia had sewn one rabbit

Tricia loved, making her feel warm, cherished and protected. She laid her head against his chest, listening to the pleasing thud of his heart.

"A Christmas baby," she murmured into his chest. "How special. They must have had her by now."

"I'll try phoning," suggested John.

James's phone was on divert to voice-mail, so he left a message saying Happy Christmas and they hoped all was well.

They took the spare stocking and filled it with goodies. Ben was fast asleep as they tiptoed in and silently swapped the stockings over.

They went to bed but Tricia was sure she wouldn't sleep until they had some news.

"Grandma, Grandma, he's been." Tricia woke with a start. Ben's excited face was inches from her own, his voice an excited whisper. It was dark still, but the landing light was always left on when Ben came to stay. "Look what Father Christmas brought me."

He shoved a hand clutching some of the stuffed toys right under her nose. "Look, look, I got rabbits, I got a lion – raaaaarrrrr. And an elephant, and a ladybird and a hedgehog. And some pens and an orange and..."

"Oh lovely," she said blearily.

"Has the new baby come yet?" asked Ben, lining up the animals on the bed.

"I don't know," said Tricia, sitting up, pushing the leaden quilt aside and feeling anxious, glancing at the clock. It was only five am, and John was an oblivious, slumbering lump beside her.

"It's still very early Ben. Do you think you could go back to bed, even for a little while?"

Two hours later, Tricia was up and about, and the turkey was roasting, filling the house with the scent of a family Christmas.

Ben was watching TV with his menagerie sitting on a cushion beside him. Tricia kept telling herself not to be silly; people had babies all the time. Things rarely went wrong nowadays. But surely, surely, they should have heard something by now?

The phone went, freezing her heart. It was James.

"Hi Mum, Morag Elspeth arrived safely at 4.37am this morning, 7lb 4 oz. After all that rush earlier, she decided to take her time after all. Emma's doing fine but very tired. I've left her sleeping, and I'll be over in about half an hour. Oh, and thanks for the message from Dad, but you really shouldn't have stayed up waiting. Happy Christmas."

Continued overleaf...

Tricia's heart swelled. "Oh, oh that's wonderful. A little granddaughter, oh…" Tricia felt a tugging on her arm. "There's a little boy wants to talk to you," she said, passing the phone to Ben.

"Is the baby here, Daddy?"

Ben smiled broadly and squealed with joy when James said, "Yes."

James looked exhausted when he arrived but greeted Ben with a huge hug. "Happy Christmas," he said, looking bemused by the animals that Father Christmas had brought.

After he answered Ben's excited questions about his new baby sister, he wilted over a cup of tea and a mince pie, and lay down for a nap on the spare bed.

"I suspect we'll be eating leftovers for quite a while," said Tricia when the Christmas dinner for three was over.

Ben's animals were ranged round a plate of turkey and vegetables, which Ben was helping them to eat – just as well, since he'd refused veg on his own plate.

At hospital visiting time, James made Ben clean his hands just like everyone else going onto the ward. This was a bit difficult because one of the rabbits was firmly welded to his fingers.

Morag Elspeth was fast asleep, rosebud mouth working dreamily, tiny fingers curled. Ben gazed at her in awe.

"I'm sorry yesterday was such a rush," said Emma to him. "We forgot your Christmas stocking, didn't we? I expect Father Christmas will have filled it anyway, even though you weren't at home." She looked pointedly at James, evidently hoping he would take the hint.

"Father Christmas came anyway," exclaimed Ben. "He didn't seem to mind that it was Grandad's boring old walking sock, and he gave me some very special things. Grandma and Grandad would only let me bring one of them."

Ben showed the little rabbit to his mum.

Emma's eyes widened with recognition, and a wistful smile played on her lips. "I remember getting something like that in my Christmas stocking," she said giving Tricia a conspiratorial wink. "Clever old Father Christmas."

"And Father Christmas gave me my name in wood. Can Daddy put that up on my door, please? And can I hold the baby?"

"Only if you're very careful and someone helps you," said Emma anxiously.

"I remember getting something like that in my Christmas stocking," smiled Emma

Tricia had been waiting for an excuse. She gently picked up the baby, who stirred, and opened her eyes. Tricia held her close and breathed in the lovely new-baby scent. Memories of Emma as a baby flooded back.

Ben settled into the armchair and Tricia carefully placed Morag in his arms. He gazed at her in wonder. "I love her. This is the best Christmas ever."

THE AUTHOR SAYS...

"My mum, a creative lady, made bunnies out of felt and cotton wool when my school was raising funds. She didn't have a pattern, just an idea."

Brain BOOSTERS

Codebreaker

Each letter of the alphabet has been replaced by a number. We've started it off – see if you can fill the grid! It should reveal the second line of a famous flower poem.

	2		20		1		16		14		11		9	
14	24	16	16	19	2	24	21		3	13	9	3	10	13
	23		3		3		22		5		26		12	
4	5	14	3	22	6		25	24	20	16	11	2	24	21
	2		25				20		6		16		16	
9	14	2	20	25						17	8	25	11	14
	2			22							12		22	
14	3	5	10	12						9	14	14	25	3
	2		9							18			20	
2	7	16	8	6						1	9	24	21	14
	25		20		16		15				22		25	
5	24	22	9	11	15	5	22		8 R	25	9	22	18	14
	25		18		3		2		16 O		8		25	
9	14	13	16	8	25		8	25	14 S	5	18	2	24	21
	14		18		24		3		25 E		14		3	

A B C D ~~E~~ F G H I J K L M N ~~O~~ P Q ~~R~~ ~~S~~ T U V W X Y Z

1	2	3	4	5	6	7	8	9	10	11	12	13
							R					
14	**15**	**16**	**17**	**18**	**19**	**20**	**21**	**22**	**23**	**24**	**25**	**26**
S		O									E	

7	2	16	22	25	3	14		9	8	25		17	22	5	25
		O		E		S			R	E					E

Solutions on page 161

The Easter Egg Hunt!

One eagerly anticipated delivery, an unexpected gift and a cheery new postman add up to chocolatey mayhem...

By Ginny Swart

Marilyn saw the postman coming up the path and opened the door before he had a chance to knock.

"Miss M Barton? A parcel for you, miss. Please sign here."

Marilyn signed with a flourish and practically snatched the box from his hands. What a star Charlie was! He'd taken the hint!

They'd been wandering hand in hand down the street one evening and she'd spotted the beautiful little enamelled egg in the window of an antique shop. It was nestling sumptuously on gold velvet and had a dark blue background with a cluster of tiny enamelled flowers and pearls circling the middle, like miniature jewels.

"Is that a Fabergé egg?" she'd asked. "I've never seen one. It's so beautiful!"

"It can't possibly be a genuine Fabergé," mused Charlie. "But it's certainly a very good imitation."

Charlie did something financial in the city and prided himself on his good taste. His flat in Kensington was beautifully furnished with carefully chosen antiques and some very nice, old Eastern rugs.

"Probably awfully expensive," said Marilyn with longing. "It would make a wonderful Easter egg for some lucky girl, wouldn't it?"

"Ah yes – but Easter eggs are meant to be chocolate, aren't they?"

"You know I'm not even thinking about chocolates," she said indignantly. "I've been sticking to this diet for months and I'm not breaking it for even one nibble of an Easter egg. Stop trying to tempt me!"

"We used to have Easter egg hunts when I was a kid," said Charlie dreamily. "My favourites were those marshmallow ones wrapped in silver paper. My mum hid them all over the garden, and one year I found nine. I wonder whether they still make those?"

"Well if they do, you'll have to eat them in secret," said Marilyn tartly. "It's

"My favourites were the marshmallow ones. Mum hid them in the garden"

Continued overleaf...

ILLUSTRATIONS: JAMES DEWAR, THINKSTOCK

She couldn't wait to open it

Continued from previous page

difficult enough sitting down to steamed fish while watching you scoff your steak and chips."

"Well, it's hard to enjoy anything with you staring at my every mouthful and making me feel guilty."

"I do not! Don't exaggerate!"

Really, although she loved everything about him, Charlie could be surprisingly insensitive sometimes. He didn't understand that her pencil-slim figure didn't come without a great deal of hard work. Not to mention mental suffering. Hours in the gym every week with a personal trainer. No bread or cake for how long – a year? Only steamed vegetables and fish and rice crackers, with a tiny serving of cheese on special occasions.

And the ridiculous remarks he made! Telling her she'd look just as good with a few extra pounds and she should learn to relax about her appearance and just enjoy herself more. She just knew he wouldn't want to be seen with her if she just gave in every time she fancied a biscuit, and turned into a fat lump. Which could easily happen if she didn't keep total control of her eating habits.

Marilyn sat down and carefully unwrapped the box. It was awfully big for something the size of a goose egg, but it had probably needed a lot of packing.

She lifted the lid and gasped.

A very large chocolate egg winked up at her from a bed of tissue paper. It was decorated with a garland of perfect little pink and white sugar flowers around the middle, and topped with a pink satin ribbon. She took a deep breath and her worst suspicions were confirmed. It was orange-flavoured dark chocolate. Her absolute favourite, and he knew it.

Her worst suspicions were confirmed. Orange-flavoured dark chocolate

How cruel of Charlie. How could he taunt her with chocolate like this? She snatched up the little note:

Custom-made for my best girl! With love.

She knew that if she phoned Charlie she might explode with indignation. So she picked up her cell phone and punched out a text:

Very funny. You know I can't eat this! How can you be so mean and heartless?

She pressed "send" so hard she practically split the little phone in two.

Then she sniffed the egg again. The smell of orange-flavoured chocolate was overwhelming, and it was lucky that she was strong enough to ignore it. Although… a whole year without chocolate.

Perhaps one little nibble wouldn't be the end of the world?

Three blocks down at Number 37, Margaret Burton heard the unfamiliar knock of the postman and shuffled slowly down the passage. Her rheumatism was especially bad this morning and she couldn't imagine why he didn't just push her bills through the letter box as he usually did.

"Parcel for you, Mrs Burton! Sign here, please."

"Good morning young man! What's happened to Fred?"

"Fred's retired, Mrs Burton. I'm Dennis."

"Well, hello, Dennis. A parcel for me? Goodness. Let me get my specs."

Margaret plodded back to her bedroom and dithered a little while she searched for her glasses. They were difficult to find when she wasn't wearing them.

Dennis waited patiently, then thrust a little machine at her.

"Put your cross here, Mrs Burton. No, I don't mean a real cross, love, your signature will do fine. Ta."

He handed over a small parcel, gave her a little salute and walked away briskly, leaving Margaret turning over the box in her hands.

What could this be? It wasn't her birthday. Her sister Alice had always remembered her birthday with a box of chocolates but since she had died three years before, no-one had remembered her with a gift of any sort. Besides, her birthday wasn't until September when she would turn eighty-seven.

Then a thought struck her. Could it be from Ben, her great-nephew? He was the only member of the family she saw these days although he hadn't been around for some time.

He was Alice's grandson and had the reputation of being a bit wild, in all sorts of trouble at school as well as later, and didn't seem to be able to hold a job for longer than a few months. After his last brush with the law, she had the feeling the rest of the family had more or less given up on him.

But from the time he was a little boy, Margaret had been charmed by his cheeky wide grin and the stream of jokes he had ready for every occasion. She was delighted that he still popped in to see her every now and then. A visit from Ben was as good as a tonic.

Could it be from Ben, her great-nephew? She hadn't seen him lately

But last time he came, after she phoned and asked him if he could mend the catch on her window, he hadn't been his usual cheerful self at all.

He'd drunk three cups of tea and finished off all her shortbread, when he heaved a sigh and started to speak seriously for the first time.

"Aunt Margie, I need to do something with my life. I'm twenty-seven and I've

Continued overleaf...

Continued from previous page

got nothing to show for it! I'm practically broke, with no job, no prospects of finding one, and not even a girlfriend."

"What happened to Lily?"

Margaret had heard all about Lily the time before and he'd even shown her a photograph of the two of them at some nightclub. One look and she'd known that Lily wasn't the right sort of girl for him, but he'd been so proud of her.

"She's history," he said briefly. "She called me a loser. And I'm beginning to think I am."

"Of course you're not," she said firmly. "You're a young man with your whole life in front of you. You just haven't found your right niche yet."

She looked at him affectionately. "That Lily was a thoughtless girl, in my opinion, letting a good lad like you slip away from her. You'll find a nice sweetheart again soon enough. And as for a job – where have you looked? Been down to the Job Centre?"

"Nothing there," he muttered. "I don't want to wash cars or deliver boxes. I need some sort of a career, Aunt Margaret, but I haven't got any qualifications. Never even learned about computers, nothing stuck when I tried that course at the Adult Ed centre."

"I don't blame you, those things are a complete mystery to me too," she said comfortably. "But you were always more practical. How about driving? You could drive one of those hire cars, maybe?"

He laughed shortly. "Not with my track record, Auntie Margaret. Don't you remember, I'm the black sheep who smashed up Dad's car when I was sixteen? And two crashes after that. The police don't think me and cars go together too well. They still haven't given me back my licence."

"Yes, well. Maybe not a driver, then. But you're so good with your hands, there must be something you can do."

Then she had a light-bulb moment. "Cakes!" she exclaimed. "Harry Roberts has a big bakery in town and I know he's always looking for staff. Wouldn't you like to try your hand at baking?"

Suddenly she had a lightbulb moment. "Cakes!" she exclaimed excitedly

"Aunt Margaret, I don't know the first thing about baking." He laughed. "Closest I've come to a cake is the one you made me for my birthday when I turned twenty-one."

"Harry would train you, of course. You'd be like an apprentice to start with."

"Yeah – me in the boardroom with Sir Alan Sugar!"

"Seriously, Ben my boy, being a baker would be a good job. You'd learn useful skills. It would be a good career, definitely. And it's secure – people have to eat, don't they?"

She could see he was considering this new idea, but he shook his head.

"He probably wouldn't take me on anyway. I'm too old to be an apprentice."

"Well, I used to teach Harry Roberts maths a long time ago and I dare say he'll remember me. I could put in a word for you, if you like."

"I guess it couldn't hurt. But I expect he'll say no."

Harry Roberts did remember his old maths teacher with great affection, and three days later Ben had started in the bakery. He began at the bottom, washing out the huge steel mixing drums for the dough, sweeping the floors and generally doing every menial job that needed doing.

That had been four years ago and to her great satisfaction, Ben had stuck it out.

He'd done so well that these days he headed Harry Robert's new confectionery section, making Turkish Delight, creamy toffees and all sorts of sweeties. Last time he'd popped in, he'd brought Margaret a big packet of his new line, white chocolate cherry whirls.

So if this parcel was from him, it was more than likely to be sweeties.

Margaret opened the box and removed layers of soft white packaging. Inside was the most exquisite bejewelled blue egg. It looked as though it was made of some sort of stone and had a circlet of colourful flowers around the middle, scattered with tiny pearls and sparkling gems. It was the most beautiful thing she'd ever seen, and when she carefully picked it up and felt the weight of it, she knew it must be old and very expensive.

It couldn't be from Ben. He simply wasn't making the sort of money that could buy a treasure like this.

There was a note on thick white paper tucked into the box:

A special Easter egg for my very special lady.

Hmmm. Definitely not from Ben, then – but maybe he could help throw some light on the mystery. She picked up the phone and dialled his number.

"Ben?"

"Hi, Auntie Margaret! Did you get that egg I sent you?"

"Yes dear, it's just arrived, thank you. It's beautiful, but –"

"I know orange-flavoured chocolate is your all-time favourite," he said proudly. "That's from my new line – hot off the press, or off the mould, I should say!"

"You sent me a chocolate egg?"

"Hi, Auntie Margaret! Did you get that egg I sent you? It's from my new line"

"Yes – don't you recognise those little sugar flowers round the middle? They're meant to be petunias, just like the ones in that pot that you put out beside your front door in the summer. I decorated that egg just for you."

Continued overleaf...

Continued from previous page

Margaret swallowed.

"That's marvellous, Ben – you're so clever. I – I just have to sort something out."

She ended the call and looked more closely at the outer wrapping. *This* parcel was addressed to a Miss M Barton at Number 57. Not Miss M Burton of Number 37. The new postman had muddled them up.

Margaret wrapped the little box again as best she could, put on her coat and headed up the road to Number 57. She just hoped Miss M Barton hadn't opened Ben's egg.

The mystery was solved

Marilyn's face was a study in horror and guilt when the mix-up was explained. Margaret couldn't help breaking into a smile when she saw the sizeable hole in what was supposed to have been *her* egg.

"My Ben does make excellent chocolate, doesn't he?" she said kindly. "No-one could resist it, I'm sure."

She knew her obliging great-nephew would be happy to make her another, once he heard about what had happened.

"I have a call to make," whispered Marilyn, reading the note that came with the little blue egg. "I need to apologise to someone I was very rude to. I wonder if he'll ever forgive me."

He did, of course.

"On one condition," said Charlie, struggling not to laugh. "You save a piece of that fabulous-sounding egg for me – and you join me tonight for steak and chips."

"All right," she said, smiling.

"And you never sit down with a plate of steamed fish again."

"Oh… All right."

It didn't feel like the end of the world at all – it felt wonderful!

There was just one thing she needed to do before she saw him tonight, she decided… go out and buy Charlie a dozen of those chocolate marshmallow Easter eggs.

She might even go so far as to try one of them herself.

THE AUTHOR SAYS… "I've always liked the idea of a mix-up and the possibilities that stem from it. And I once saw an egg just like the one I described in an antique shop, and have never forgotten it."

Teatime Treat

Blueberry Scones and Jam

Ingredients

- **350g self-raising flour**
- **75g butter**
- **75g + 2tbsp caster sugar**
- **125g dried blueberries, chopped**
- **175ml + 1tbsp milk**
- **Jam and clotted cream, to serve**

1 Preheat oven to 220˚C, Fan Oven 200˚C, Gas Mark 7.

2 Sift flour in a bowl. Add butter and rub into the flour until the mixture resembles breadcrumbs.

3 Stir in 75g sugar and blueberries. Make a well in the centre and add 175ml milk. Bring together with your hands, then knead gently on a lightly floured surface.

4 Roll out the dough until 2.5cm thick. Using a 5cm plain round cutter, stamp out 16 rounds.

5 Arrange on a prepared baking tray. Brush and dust with remaining milk and sugar. Bake for about 10min until risen and golden. Cool on a wire rack. Serve warm with jam and cream.

RECIPE: KATHRYN HAWKINS PHOTOGRAPHY: STUART MACGREGOR

A Mother's Day Treat

The restaurant was Mum's dream – but now she wasn't here, it was down to Eleanor to make this day special...

By Jan Snook

es, of course it will be fine," Eleanor said, frowning, "but Mother's Day is supposed to be really special. I'm just afraid that people will be expecting something... well, more exciting than our little restaurant can provide, I suppose."

"Well, we're booked solid," her husband Dave said, "so I don't know what you're worried about. Your father's really looking forward to it."

"And that's another thing. He'll be here on Sunday, and he did lend us the money to start up. I don't want to let him down."

David opened his mouth to speak, but Eleanor carried on.

"I spoke to him yesterday, and he started on about how busy we must be, what with Mother's Day on Sunday, and how proud Mum would have been if she'd... well, still been around to see it."

She walked over to the window and looked out at the garden where daffodils were clumped in yellow patches near the summerhouse. "I suppose I think if she were here, she'd somehow manage to make it more special."

Dave put an arm round his wife's shoulder. "You're the creative one – you can make it special," he said gently.

"But how?"

"Sorry," Dave said, dropping a kiss on the top of her head and heading back towards the kitchen, "not my department. You'll think of something."

Eleanor's shoulders slumped. Later in the year, when it was warmer, children would play in the beautiful secluded garden. It was one of the reasons they had bought this country restaurant, rather than something in town.

She'd dreamed of a glass of wine in the summerhouse before opening

She smiled, remembering her dream of sitting in the summerhouse having a glass of wine before they opened in the evening. As if they ever had time!

Eleanor gave herself a little shake and went to fetch a neat stack of starched linen napkins. She started to fold them into pretty fans, ready for each place

Continued overleaf...

ILLUSTRATIONS: MANDY DIXON

Their mum had passed on her love of cooking

Continued from previous page

setting. What could she do to make Sunday different? She looked around the small dining-room, visualising it on Mother's Day, every table occupied.

They'd been open nearly a year now, and although it was a very small restaurant – thirty covers at most – they were doing OK. Her father was right: her mother would have loved it. It had been her mother's dream to open a restaurant, and it was she who had instilled a love of cooking in Eleanor in early childhood.

Eleanor could see her now, floury and aproned, helping Eleanor and her brother to roll out biscuits, overseeing their first attempts at icing and extravagantly admiring the over-decorated results. Not many children had that privilege today. Most mothers were simply too busy.

Eleanor stopped in mid-napkin: perhaps that was the answer. She frowned and looked around the room again, then went into the kitchen where Dave was making pastry.

"Any idea what the weather's supposed to be doing on Sunday?" she asked.

"Not warm enough to eat outside." He laughed. "Not in March, anyway."

"I wasn't thinking about that, quite. But would the summerhouse be warm enough for the kids – just for a little while, I mean?"

"Probably, but there's not much room in there. And it would need tidying up."

"I think I'll go and do just that." She gave him a brilliant smile and went out into the garden.

Out of the wind, the summerhouse was really quite warm. And by the time she had cleared out the rubbish, moved the croquet set and dusted the cobwebs off the beams, it really looked quite presentable. Once she'd set it up, maybe added the bunting they'd used for their opening and brightened it up with some daffodils, it should be absolutely fit for purpose. Eleanor went back inside smiling, ready to make a shopping list.

Sunday arrived, cool but sunny, and the restaurant was soon full of happy families. When most people had finished their meals and the adults had ordered coffee, Eleanor rounded up the children – who ranged from four to seven – and led them out to the summerhouse, where she clad them all in small green aprons. Then she introduced them to the icing bags full of pretty pastel icings, and the bowls of hundreds and thousands, silver balls, tiny stars, coloured sugar crystals and chocolate vermicelli. Then she brought out the trays of shaped cookies she and Dave had made the day before.

"Yes, we'll need all of these. Some will get broken and some will get eaten!"

"Surely we won't need this many, will we?" Dave had asked when she'd explained her plan to him.

"Of course we will." She'd laughed. "Some will get broken, some will be too messy and some will get eaten!"

When the children looked at all the laid-out decorations their eyes sparkled.

Eleanor showed them how to hold the icing bags and guided their hands as they practised on baking paper.

"Now," she said to the most competent little girl, "do you think you're ready to decorate a cookie for your mum?"

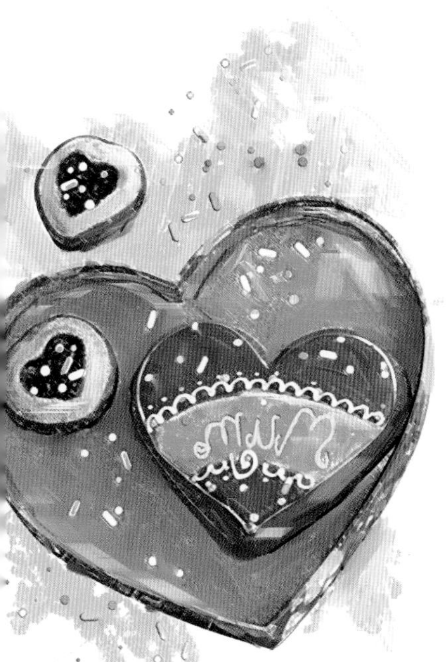

Soon there were sprinkles everywhere

A cacophony of shrill voices replied, "I am! Me too! What about my granny? Can she have a cookie? I'm having tea with my other nan, she'd like one…"

Soon there was icing everywhere, M-U-M had been spelled out in many colours and more than one child had icing in their hair. As soon as each child had finished, they went carefully back to the restaurant to present their cookies to their mothers and grandmothers. When the last child had finished, Eleanor walked back into the restaurant, wiping a stray lock of hair from her forehead.

The room was unusually animated: everyone seemed to be laughing, and the cookies were proudly displayed on nearly every table. As she weaved her way between the diners, several stopped her to thank her.

"Great idea," a man in his early thirties said, as Eleanor passed his table. He was sitting with his mother and his wife, drinking coffee. He got up, followed her to the bar, and touched her on the elbow.

"I know this isn't quite the idea," he said, "but do you think I could have a go, at the cookies, I mean?"

"Yes, of course," Eleanor said, surprised. She led him across to the summerhouse, and went inside.

"It's a bit of a mess now, I'm afraid," she said, as they surveyed the sprinkle-scattered table, "and I haven't got an apron your size…"

"I'll be fine." He smiled, starting to ice.

"You've done this before," she said admiringly as deftly he wrote *For Mum with Love* on a cookie.

"Mum let us all cook when we were kids," he said. "We were lucky. And she was looking a bit wistfully at everyone else's cookies," he added, grinning.

There was one cookie left un-iced on the table. He picked it up and gave Eleanor a questioning look. She nodded.

He iced the cookie carefully, then surveyed the results.

They returned to his table together, where the cookies were duly presented.

"Thank you," his mother said, tears in her eyes. But Eleanor was watching his wife, who was cradling her swollen tummy protectively, and smiling down at her cookie: *Happy Mother's Day, with love from the Bump!*

THE AUTHOR SAYS…

"Our neighbour owns a small restaurant, and is always anxious about guests not enjoying their meal on Mother's Day: it set me to wondering what she could do…"

Clean & Clear

There's nothing like housework to take your mind off a problem – but today even that wasn't helping Wendy...

By Brenda Crickmar

Wendy paused. Her pink feather duster, which was halfway between removing an invisible cobweb from the coving and the equally invisible dust at the top of the picture frame, paused with her.

The smile that tugged at the side of her mouth was wistful as she stared at the framed photograph on the wall before her. It portrayed a good-looking, laughing family group, typical of many that graced homes the length and breadth of the country.

In the photo her hair was sleek and shining: her husband Mike, despite his glasses and thinning hair, still handsome, but it was on her son's face that her eyes lingered longest.

Robbie, their beloved son Robbie with his thick, dark hair and his cheeky grin, aged – what? Twenty-one, maybe twenty-two? Her heart filled with love at the sight of him.

The pink feather duster flicked over the glass and with a sigh, Wendy moved on.

Now, a decade later, she had to acknowledge that they hadn't turned out to be much of a family after all.

As a teenager Wendy had dreamed of finding the perfect man, settling down and producing the textbook home and family. And on the outside at least, it seemed she'd been successful. Her eyes strayed again to the perfect family group, all teeth and smiles – so much of it was a lie.

Why had Robbie turned out to be such a rebel? After all, she and Mike had provided a stable home that was surely a model of respectability. From average beginnings they'd worked steadily together to build a life where Robbie could enjoy all the things they'd missed out on as children.

Her eyes strayed again to the perfect family group... so much of it was a lie

But Robbie hadn't really cared. Sure, he'd opened his presents, said thank you nicely, but he'd always rather be off, away from home, on a bike he'd never really looked after, exploring pastures new.

"Oh Robbie," she remembered saying, absolutely aghast at the sight of his

Continued overleaf...

ILLUSTRATIONS: THINKSTOCK, KIRK HOUSTON

Wendy paused in front of the family photograph

Continued from previous page

newly pierced ear. "Why did you have to do that?"

"It's cool Mum," said Robbie, his eyes dancing with mischief.

"But Robbie, your lovely hair," she'd almost wailed when he'd come home with the shaven haired look.

"No pleasing you, is there Mum?" Robbie had remonstrated. "Last month you were on at me to get it cut!"

"Leave him alone," said Mike from the sidelines. "He's young. He'll settle."

"But he'll never amount to anything if he goes on at this rate," said Wendy. "He doesn't do his course work. He's out till all hours – and his music... Well, how can you call it music?" She rolled her eyes heavenward in despair.

And she'd been right, hadn't she?

Despite the chance of a university education, he'd dropped out claiming academia wasn't for him; that he was a free spirit.

Unable to hide the disappointment in her eyes, Wendy had turned away.

Mike had been more accepting.

"Things have changed," he told her. "This generation don't seem to grow up quite as fast as we did. When I think of the responsibilities we foisted upon ourselves when we were barely into our twenties... Jobs for life, mortgages, a baby." He gave a sigh.

"Surely you don't regret any of that?" asked Wendy in alarm. "Look at what we've achieved." She gestured around her and towards the new patio that lay outside the modern folding doors then beyond that, to the tidy lawn and shrubs in the immaculate garden.

Mike smiled and ruffled her hair, which she immediately smoothed again.

"Of course I don't. Different times that's all. Only sometimes I think it might

Wendy put down her duster and went into the kitchen

have been good to have taken off with just a rucksack."

"Well, I don't!" Wendy was unable to suppress a shiver of revulsion. "Getting lost, eating strange food; some of those countries are not exactly hygienic you know. Not knowing where you'll be sleeping that night..."

"Well anyway, it didn't arise did it? If you didn't get into one of the few universities, it would never occur to you to take a lengthy vacation, bumming around." Mike smiled and shrugged. "That was just for students – if they were lucky."

Thinking of this now, Wendy went through to her modern kitchen. Shiny white units, black granite surfaces and the very latest coffee machine; a coffee machine she couldn't actually be bothered to use just for herself. She filled the kettle, reached for a jar of instant, and a china mug.

The envelope was there on the table where she'd thrown it earlier as though she couldn't bear to contemplate its contents.

Recognising Robbie's scrawl instantly, she'd eagerly picked it up from the front door mat. Perhaps he's coming home, she'd thought. Perhaps after twelve years of a Nomadic lifestyle, selling holidays or time shares, instructing surf boarding, or ski-ing; even at one time working as a chalet maid… A chalet maid – for goodness sake! Her son Robbie, when she'd had such high hopes for him!

Oh, she still loved him, of course she did. But there was something now in her attitude that verged on the indulgent, rather than the proud.

And she'd so wanted to be proud.

"Heard from Robbie lately," her friends would ask. And she'd laugh carelessly. "Oh yes, he's having a marvelous time," she'd say, and go on that he was in Mexico or in Austria or wherever. Then she'd add that he always kept in touch. But she didn't say that most of his communications were in the form of jokes sent by e-mail, or that they hadn't seen him now for over a year. Somehow it was too heart-breaking to admit to that.

But first thing this morning she'd pounced on the letter. The stamp showed it was from Phuket, so he still hadn't moved on. Wendy's mouth had formed a little moue of resignation. For the past year he'd been working as an estate agent out there. Mike had taken that as a good sign.

"Lucky devil. All that lovely weather," he'd said.

The envelope was large and felt thick beneath her fingers. Maybe he'd sent a longer letter this time. Although that would be unlike him. Most of his e-mails were short and betrayed little of his lifestyle, which resignedly Wendy had come to imagine as being that of a beach bum. As for a letter – it was a rarity.

With hands that were surprisingly shaky, she'd torn at the envelope.

A photograph dropped out and landed face side down.

On the back three words were written. *Your granddaughter Lily-Mae.*

What? What? Feverishly, Wendy scoured the accompanying single sheet of paper.

Robbie had been with Lily-Mae's mother Rose – "I call her Rose, I can't pronounce her Thai name"– for a year now, he explained. They were very happy together. Would she and Dad consider coming out for a visit?

Wendy had sat down right then and there on the stairs and cried.

No more dreams of Robbie coming home and settling down with a nice English girl and living only a car drive away. No more looking forward to family Christmases, or taking the grandchildren to the zoo.

Wendy wept for her lost future.

Oh Robbie, she thought, *how could you do this to us?*

Then she began to feel angry as well as injured. She thought about Robbie, the disappointments he'd handed out over the years. Why couldn't he have worked

Continued overleaf…

The envelope, with Robbie's scrawl on the front, felt thick beneath her fingers

Continued from previous page

towards a life like their kind of life; a life that included a lovely family photograph on the wall?

She'd wanted to phone Mike at work and let go a tirade of upset and fury, but she didn't. It was spring and she'd planned to clean. With a face that wore a thousand reproaches she'd pulled out the vacuum cleaner...

Now, as she sipped at her coffee, she discovered it was almost scalding and took a perverse delight in the fact that it burnt her lip. That was her son's fault too!

Then she gave a self-deprecating grin at her stupidity.

Mike was right!

The confines of a conventional life were not for Robbie. She remembered his zest for new faces and places; how his enjoyment of life lit up a room when he walked into it.

Love is not conditional, she told herself. *He can't live our life. We can't live his.*

Hesitantly, she eased the photo out of its envelope again.

Creamy skin, tuft of black hair, mouth like a little rosebud. A new life.

Her granddaughter was beautiful!

Lily-Mae – a little girl. Wendy had always wanted a girl. Prayed for one after Robbie was born, but it hadn't happened – till now.

Trying for calm, she straightened her shoulders and picked up the phone.

After three rings, Mike answered.

"Hi sweetheart, what are you up to?"

"Oh, only cleaning," answered Wendy, tasting for a moment the rage she'd felt earlier and the need to translate it into some form of physical activity. Should she pass on her feelings of powerless frustration? Mike would soothe her in the way that he was good at, and always did.

Surprised to find that the enforced curve of her lips had stretched to the semblance of a smile, she took a deep breath.

"Mike, I've got the most marvellous news," she started shakily. "I was going to wait until you arrived home but in the end, I just couldn't... Oh Mike, you'll never guess..." her voice suddenly caught on a hic-cup. "We've got the most beautiful granddaughter, and – and Robbie's asked us to go and visit!"

"My word," said Mike after a long moment. "He's full of surprises, isn't he? But – why are you crying?"

A few more sobs escaped her as through her tears she felt her smile stretch to a beam. "Oh Mike, I'm just so happy..."

Lily-Mae was beautiful

THE AUTHOR SAYS... **"Sometimes life doesn't pan out the way you'd hoped, but after a bout of cleaning or gardening, somehow, it doesn't seem quite so bad!"**

Fancy That!

Spring flower facts to wow you!

◆ The Romans were the first to celebrate births and birthdays with flowers.

◆ **Scilly money! Prince Charles is paid one daffodil a year rent for his land on the Island of Scilly.**

◆ Apple blossom is the state flower of Arkansas.

◆ **"Snowdrops" was the British nickname for American military police officers stationed in the UK during the Second World War, because of their white helmets.**

The Loddon Lily is the county flower of Berkshire

◆ **Mother's Day founder Anna Jarvis chose the carnation as the emblem of the celebration in 1907.**

Crocuses were first cultivated on the island of Crete

◆ Hyacinth was a beautiful youth from Greek mythology.

◆ **A tussie-mussie was the Victorian name for a small posy.**

Dewberry leaves can be used to make tea

Temporarily planting camomile near an ailing plant will revive it

◆ The heather crab spider can change colour to suit the flowers it lurks in.

◆ **Good King Henry, Perennial Goosefoot, Lincolnshire Spinach and Poor-man's Asparagus are all names for cottage garden favourite Chenopodium bonus-henricus.**

WORDS: DOUGLAS MCPHERSON PICTURES: ALAMY, THINKSTOCK

Spring Baby

Can the season of our birth really influence what we love and the shape of our personality for the rest of our lives?

By Douglas McPherson

Jasmine was a spring baby. The first six months of her life were summer. Her mother parked her pram in the garden; she gazed at the blue sky and felt the warmth of the sun on her face.

Dan was an autumn boy; the first six months of his life were winter. He chortled at indoor parties and enjoyed the warmth of central heating.

Neither Jasmine nor Dan could remember the first six months of their lives. But at the age of twenty-six, Jasmine was a summer girl. She loved the outdoors, the countryside and beach. She dreaded the short days of winter and the rain and snow that would keep her indoors.

Dan didn't mind the summer – it was when he met Jasmine, after all. How carefree she looked in her summer dress, with the sun in her hair. Their courtship, country walks and pub lunches, only caused minor tensions because she liked to eat in the garden and he, in the bar.

Dan compromised and ate in the garden – under the sunshade. Secretly, he looked forward to winter, when they could cuddle up indoors beside a roaring fire. Because Dan was a winter boy.

Dan loved Christmas – the parties, the dinners, the indoor-ness of it all. Jasmine enjoyed all of that, because she loved being with Dan. But her favourite parts of winter were the crisp, bright mornings when she could get out in the open and catch the first scent of spring.

Jasmine sometimes wished Dan liked the outdoors more, but he preferred Sundays indoors with the papers – and if he was happy, she was happy.

Dan would have liked a winter wedding, with snow falling like confetti. Jasmine wouldn't have minded marrying in winter, as long as they could go abroad and tie the knot on a sun-kissed beach. Dan didn't think that would be the same, and he didn't like spending too long on beaches anyway.

So they married in June, when the countryside was blooming. Jasmine looked more beautiful to him than ever, and she'd never felt happier, because Jasmine was a summer girl.

Dan would have liked a winter wedding, with snow falling softly like confetti

Jasmine was delighted when Tom was born in the spring. The summer stretched ahead of her – parks, beaches, rivers and sunny lanes. There was so much to show her beautiful boy.

Continued overleaf...

Jasmine's pram was parked out in the garden

Continued from previous page

Jasmine had a mild case of the post-baby blues when Chloe came along a year later. It was autumn, after all, and Jasmine always felt a bit down as winter drew in. Dan was happy to take up the slack. He loved being indoors with his beautiful new baby, rocking her in the kitchen by the warmth of the range.

The seasons turned and the children grew. Dan enjoyed kicking a ball about in the park with Tom, because that's what Tom wanted to do. Dan tried to interest his son in model trains or stamp collecting – the passions of his own childhood. But Tom was an outdoor boy.

Tom was an outdoor boy

Jasmine loved gardening. Dan and Tom helped her with the heavy work, like digging and mowing the lawn – although

Looking fondly at their children, they marvelled at how different they were

Dan liked to get such tasks out of the way, so he could go inside and watch the football on TV. Tom was football-mad too, but he preferred to be outside, actually playing the game with his mates.

Jasmine wished her daughter was more interested in flowers and birds, or just relaxing in the sun and spotting patterns in the fluffy white clouds. But Chloe took after her father. Chloe liked reading, cooking and making things indoors. Because Chloe was an indoor girl.

And so life went on, in sun and showers, wind and snow. And, for all their differences, the four of them rubbed along contentedly.

Tom got a job as a park ranger and in time became a rugged, outdoorsy dad. Chloe loved office life and home life, too. After she married and had children, she kept an immaculate house full of tasty cooking.

Sometimes, at family gatherings, Jasmine and Dan looked at their children and marvelled at how different they were. Of course, Jasmine and Dan were quite different themselves.

But they never stopped to wonder whether maybe it was simply because she was a spring baby – and he was an autumn boy.

THE AUTHOR SAYS...

"This story came from realising that I am indoorsy while my partner is outdoorsy – I was born in November while she was born in May."

Brain BOOSTERS

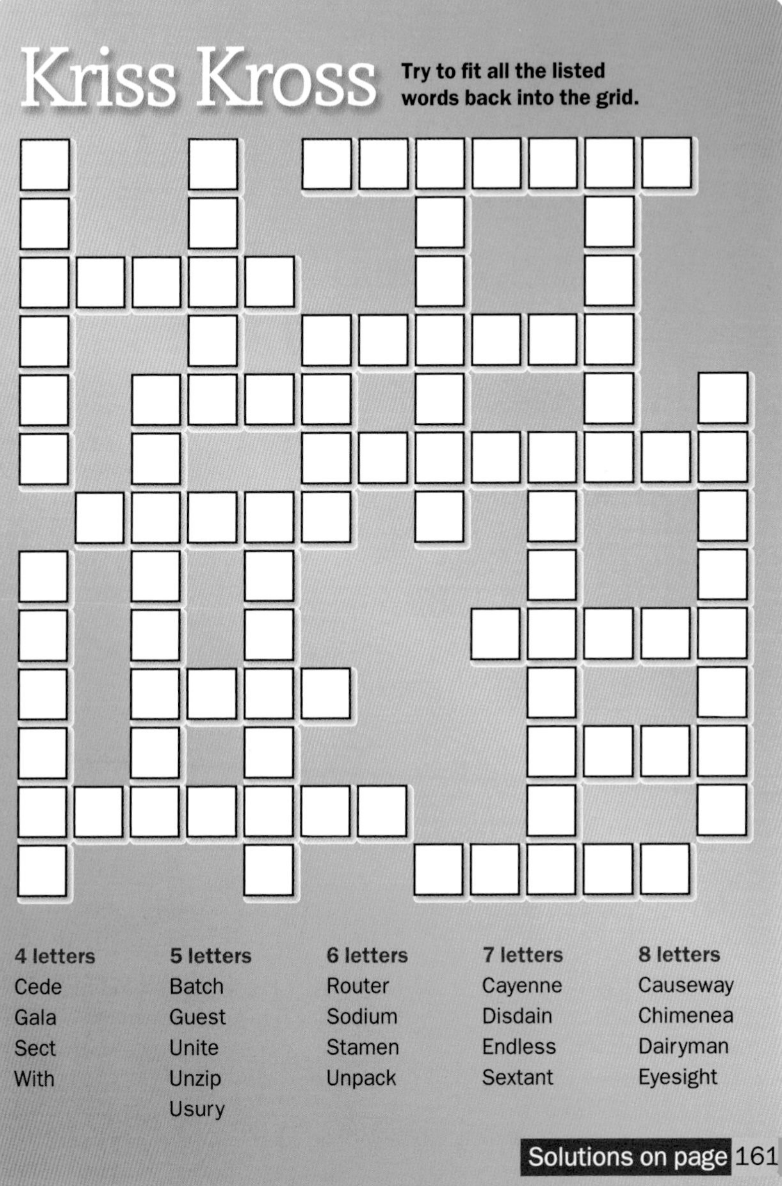

Solutions on page 161

No Strings Attached!

When two people are meant to meet, the Universe will find a way to make it happen – even if it takes a little while

By Elizabeth Bendall

"Fifteen hundred pounds?" the old lady gasped. "But only last week I saw a bass just like it on the *Antiques Roadshow* valued at five thousand. Please, my husband was in the Bellman Philharmonic – it must be worth more."

David looked doubtful. The instrument didn't even have strings.

"My father would know more. I'm only standing in for him while he's in hospital. If you could bring it back next month…"

"I'm seventy-six, young man," she said crisply. "Are you seriously suggesting I take a double bass home and return with it next month?"

"Done!" said the woman before he could blink.

Writing out the cheque, David couldn't help thinking he very probably had been.

Thirty minutes later he was engrossed in a copy of Antique Times when an increase in traffic noise told him someone had just come in. He looked up into Bambi-brown eyes and an elfin face.

"May I help?" he asked, thinking how exquisitely pretty the girl was.

"Yes, I'm interested in that," she said. "A Barnabetti, isn't it?"

He followed her gaze, expecting "that" to be an oil painting. There was the double bass, lolling against the wall like a drunk at closing time.

Someone came into the shop; he looked into Bambi-brown eyes and an elfin face

She had a point. It was bigger than her and they'd had an almighty struggle getting it out of the taxi.

"OK," he said slowly. "How about two thousand upfront and whatever profit it makes we split fifty-fifty?"

Nooo, roared his absent parent in his head. *A deal's a deal, never hold out the prospect of more.*

"It's only just come in." He grinned. "Haven't checked the barcode yet!"

The girl smiled indulgently. "Well, it's definitely French. Let's have a look." Kneeling, she put her eye to the scroll-shaped gap, angling her head to see inside. "Good, there's a label. Got a torch?"

"Certainly," he said, dragging his gaze

Continued overleaf…

He thought she was exquisitely pretty

Continued from previous page

from the enticing band of suntanned skin where her T-shirt had pulled free of her jeans. "There you go."

Taking the penlight, she shone it in the gap. "C-h-a-r-l…" Abruptly she jerked upright. "I was wrong. It's not a Barnabetti, it's a Charles Nicholas Gand, dated 1864." Holding the bass by the neck, she swung it on its spike. "Needs a lot of work," she said, tracing the cracks in the crazed varnish, "but it's sound. How much are you asking for it?"

"We-ell…" he hedged, Stradivarian-sized price tags crowding his brain. "I thought maybe… four thousand?"

He waited for the shrieks of derision.

"Hmm," she mused. "Fair, given its condition. OK, I'll take it. Give me an hour. My name's Jo James. Don't go selling it to anyone else now."

He was still trying to think of a witty riposte when the door clicked shut behind her.

He eyed the double bass. Four grand for that? It had to be a wind-up, surely? That made two women who'd seen him coming today! Chuckling to himself, he went back to his magazine.

He was halfway through lunch when a bang on the door made the *Closed* sign bounce. The girl's face was pressed to the glass, like a child gazing in at a sweetshop. In the No Parking spot behind her was a beat-up old van.

Putting his bacon sandwich back on the plate, he went to open the door.

"I have to be quick," she told him, as soon as he unlocked, "Double yellow."

Unzipping a holdall, she took out eight wads of money one after the other, slapping them on the counter like a gangster settling a debt. A maroon bass cover followed, which she flipped open with the expertise of a chambermaid opening out a bed-sheet.

"How come you know so much about these things?" he asked, watching her manoeuvre it over the hourglass body.

"Dad's a restorer," she told him. "Basses, cellos, anything stringed. In a month you won't recognise this. Be an angel and grab the bag for me, please?"

She was already lugging the instrument to the door. The woman was a human dynamo. Stuffing the receipt in the holdall, he shot after her.

"I was wondering," he began, hovering by the van.

"Yes?" Jo asked, unlocking the rear door and sliding the bass inside.

"I'd, er, really like to see…"

"The finished article?" she cut in, as a determined-looking traffic warden approached. "I'll let you know when it's ready. Must fly!"

Grabbing the bag she jumped in, and started up the engine.

"Thanks for your help, er…"

"David," he supplied.

She shook his hand. "I'll be in touch, David."

In a roar of acceleration she was off, leaving David gazing after her. He ran his

Three weeks crawled by with David wishing every day he'd got her number

fingers lightly over the palm of his empty hand. Who'd said anything about it being the bass he wanted to see?

Three weeks crawled by, with David wishing every day that he'd thought to ask for Jo's number. Then, one morning, he arrived at the shop to find a note on the mat. The fully restored bass would be making its "debut" that evening at The Belvedere. *Come if you can,* Jo had written. *No strings!*

Ten hours later he was in the concrete cellar that was fast becoming the town's hottest nightspot, The Belvedere. He scanned the sea of faces, looking for Jo, but she didn't seem to be there. He was about to head for the bar when the lights dimmed and there was a sudden explosion of fast, toe-tapping jazz.

There was Jo, her slender body hunched over the bass, her fingers flying over the strings. David stood enthralled by her skill. Catching his eye, she grinned and winked. A honeyed glow seeped through his veins.

No strings, Jo had said, but there'd be strings alright – he'd make sure of it!

"When your other half's a double bass player, living with these giant instruments is part of the deal. I suppose it was inevitable I'd eventually feature one in a story!"

Under The Wisteria

Solitude and the peace of rural France work their healing magic on Claire – but then a stranger moves in…

By Sarah Bartle

By November, William was gone. Almost immediately I succumbed to bronchitis with coughing and chest pains until in February my children said, in desperation, that for my sixtieth birthday they'd pay for me to have a long, restful vacation.

So, soon after Easter, I pulled into the courtyard of a small French house containing two self-contained apartments. Only the entrance hall and the garden would be shared. But how was I going to cope alone?

The front door was ajar so I went in and found the flat I would call home for the next six months. It was light and cool and easy for housekeeping.

More delightful still was the patio that faced south towards the mountains. There, a rampant wisteria covered a wooden trellis, giving dappled shade over the rough stone slabs, and great mauve flowers like bunches of grapes skimmed my hair.

The days fled and as I spent many hours resting under the wisteria, my bronchitis disappeared.

But all too soon, I was told that my neighbour would be arriving the next day. My idyll was over.

However, common courtesy made it impossible for us to ignore each other entirely. Anyway it would have been very hard to ignore a handsome, grey-haired man such as Monsieur Ladoux. We'd smile at each other as we shared the terrace, each bringing out our morning chocolate as the sun swung round. We were happy to be friendly – but at arm's length.

Soon I started to take walks around the village. I saw the brown earth turn to green; winter wheat begin to show ears; and eventually sunflowers bloom – huge yellow patches decorating the rolling landscape.

On one hot, steamy day I made a jug of lemonade that I took outside to my table. I flopped down and poured myself a glass. Monsieur Ladoux was busy writing as usual. Without thinking I called over, "Would you like a glass of lemonade, monsieur?"

"Oh, thank you very much. You are most kind."

Continued overleaf…

ILLUSTRATIONS: MANDY MURRAY

The wisteria cast dappled shade over the patio

Continued from previous page

"Do come over here and sit down. I've been walking and am worn out in this heat!"

"Indeed, it is hot."

We sipped our drinks making small talk, and then he thanked me gravely and returned to his writing.

Almost every day after that, one or the other of us would cross the patio with the offer of a drink or maybe a piece of fruit. Never were these visits more than a few minutes, but I enjoyed them.

Eventually I said, "I hate being so formal. Please call me Claire."

He laughed. "You sound like my daughters. They can't understand why I'm still in the caves. But I prefer it this way."

"How many daughters have you?"

"Two – Michelle and Madelaine. They live not far from my home."

"I've only one daughter but I do have two sons."

"Do you see much of them?"

"Oh, yes. They live nearby, too."

He went into his apartment and returned with a bowl of peaches.

"Help yourself. I'll go and make coffee.

Momentarily he seemed to forget me, his eyes troubled. Then he shook himself

Do you take it black or white?"

"Black, please. No sugar."

"Ah! How to keep a slim figure."

I had to smile. Slim I'm not!

"And I'm Pierre."

"Hello, Pierre. I'm pleased to meet you," and I held out my hand.

He said, "Hello, Claire, your name suits you – although you are getting more golden now."

"Thank you, kind sir! But putting more weight on, too!"

"Tut! What does it matter? You young people think too much about being like shadows."

Young people, indeed! But I did preen just a little bit.

Another day, after he had shopped for lunch, he asked me to eat with him. At first we were rather stiff, but gradually we relaxed together and enjoyed our bread and cheeses with a glass of local red wine.

I said, "I've noticed you busy writing. Don't you ever use a word processor or a typewriter?"

Later I asked him, "What do you write – or is it a secret?"

"No, not a secret at all. It's a biography really, but not about a single person. It's about a village and the area round it – the place where I lived for most of my life.

"Sounds interesting. Have you done much writing before?"

"No, not really – only stuffy old medical papers and articles. This is really quite different."

"So you're a doctor?"

"Yes, like my father before me, until I retired a couple of years ago – the same village as well."

For a moment he seemed to forget me, his eyes troubled. Then he shook himself and said, "Memories have a habit of ganging up on you, Claire. I was

thinking of my father. He was killed on the way to visit a patient and I don't think that Mama ever got over it. They'd been so close."

"My parents were, too. They died in my twenties."

"I've had a good life and a very happy marriage, but my mother never smiled again – always had a void in her life. I understood that better when I lost my own wife. But what about you? Tell me about yourself."

"My life has been terribly dull, really."

"Well, let me be the judge of that."

I was reluctant to go on. Pierre noticed my hesitation and said, "If it's too painful, Claire, you don't have say anything – but Doctor Pierre would say that a little confession is good for the health."

I had to laugh. "There's nothing to confess – it's all rather sad really. After school I went to art college, but I met my husband and left to get married – we were head over heels in love.

"We had our family fairly quickly and were all very happy and content until…"

"Until?"

"A car accident. I was driving, with William beside me. Someone rammed the side where he was sitting. He was very badly injured – the other man died.

"After a long time he got back to work but was never the same again. He would have rages when his disabilities got in the way and… sometimes he blamed me for the accident."

Pierre put his hand on my arm.

"I'm so sorry, Claire. These things can happen after an accident."

"It went on for some years, then he had a stroke. He'd get nearly better and return to work, and then he would succumb again. Eventually he had to take early retirement."

"Oh, Claire!"

"By this time he was like another child. He would hardly let me out of his sight – it was difficult even to go shopping for food. But I had a good cleaning lady who

Continued overleaf…

Continued from previous page

would stand no nonsense if I went out for a few hours. Our children too would relieve me sometimes, but by then they had their own families. It was all very difficult – but not unusual, I know."

"True, but that doesn't make it any easier."

"No – and you see, when William died quite unexpectedly last autumn I blamed myself for not taking more care of him, even wondering if I could have avoided that accident."

"And what did your children say to that?"

"Told me not to be such an idiot!"

Pierre smiled. "Quite right! They knew that you had done your best."

He added, "I think the doctor would advise us to have another coffee and take a little armagnac after all that heart-searching. Will you join me?"

Strangely I felt a sense of relief. I'd never talked so openly before.

"I'd love a cup – the drink too."

Later, the easiness of that day seemed to cloud over and our ways scarcely crossed. I couldn't understand the coolness. Then one morning I was sitting on the terrace when to my surprise Pierre came out to my table.

"Good morning, Claire. How are you this lovely morning?"

"Extremely well, thank you. And you?"

"Good – all the better for seeing you."

I smiled up at him and was surprised that he looked so serious. Something was still bothering him.

"Sit down," I said. "Instead of hovering about like a black cloud."

He laughed and sat down. "I'm going shopping. Would you like to come along?"

"What a lovely idea! What time are you leaving?"

"About ten?"

"Great! Time to do a few jobs, then go with a clear conscience."

By ten o'clock we were driving along chatting amicably, all the restraint having disappeared.

It was nearly midday by the time we'd finished shopping. Pierre asked me where I'd like to eat.

"I'm sorry – I've no idea. I've not been out this way before ."

"Let me choose, then."

We drove into the mountains until we reached a small hotel beside a little river.

"Don't be put off by its appearance. The restaurant is excellent. I hope we can get in. Stay here while I go and ask."

He was soon back, smiling.

"All set – about half an hour. Why don't we wander in the village until then, stretch our legs a bit."

We walked at the edge of the river into the jumbled maze of old grey houses brightened by petunias and geraniums hanging from every window, then made our way back to the hotel and our table overlooking the water. During our meal

I felt that Pierre was withdrawing again. Something was wrong... but what ?

Later we had coffee at a small riverside table in the shade of weeping willows.

"This is lovely," Pierre said, but he sighed and I looked at him sharply.

"What's wrong, Pierre?"

He stared at the water for a long time, then without turning his head said quietly, "I have a bad conscience, Claire. I'm afraid I've been dishonest with you."

"What do you mean?"

"I told you that I had lost my wife. In a way that's true, but not in the way you believed it. Hélène's still alive, but in a nursing home. I often go to see her. She doesn't know me now, but is in good health apart from her mind. I remember your saying that your husband became like a child who was not going to grow up. I felt very guilty then – I could have so easily told you about Hélène, but the moment passed."

I put out my hand to him. "Oh, Pierre, I'm so sorry. And why should you tell a virtual stranger? I'm just glad that when you've been withdrawn, it was not me that was the cause."

"But that's where you're wrong. You are the cause – I've become far too fond of you while living my lie. And I think you like me too!"

I'm too old for coyness and smiled my agreement. "Yes, I do. But you haven't broken my heart by your confession."

His smile was rueful. "I'm selfish enough to be a bit sad about that, but it's probably better that way. Now, I've only a week of my rental left and unfortunately I can't extend. Why don't we spend more time together? Do a bit of exploring?"

"That would be wonderful!"

And it was – but by unspoken agreement, we did not let our emotions get out of hand. It would have been all too easy. But I had no wish to take such a step and Pierre seemed to understand.

When he left, our farewell was very subdued. He kissed me on both cheeks,

"I've become far too fond of you while living my lie. And I think you like me"

saying quietly, "Don't forget what I said last night, chérie."

"I won't."

Then he got into his car and disappeared from the courtyard.

Back in my apartment, already I felt the cold gloom of loneliness. Maybe – one day – there would be a shared life for Pierre and me.

In the meantime I would have to remember his words from the previous night. "I'm planning to return next year, Claire. Why don't you come too – soon after Easter?"

I had kissed him gently and his arms had tightened round me. We stood like that for a long time, then I pulled away.

"Goodnight, dear Pierre. Let's plan to meet when the wisteria starts to bloom again."

THE AUTHOR SAYS...

"This was inspired by places in France that my family loved. Human characters are partly taken from people whom I have met over the years, but never in this context."

A Fair Day At The Fayre

Luke was footloose and fancy-free and wanted to stay that way – until one fine summer day at the trading fayre...

By Pamela Kavanagh

Luke Tabbet tramped along the road to Beeston Fayre, the sun on his face, his goods and his gear on his back. May had come in warmly, spreading blossoms and birdsong over the fickle face of April.

Luke blessed the coming of summer, for the winter this time had been bleak. Early snow followed by frosts had locked the land in an iron grip, putting paid to the usual seasonal work from which he drew his sustenance. Hedging, ditching, ploughing – Luke could turn a hand to most things and prided himself on being his own man. Not for him the indignity of the Hiring Fayre, lined up with other hopefuls bearing about your person some token to show your trade. A wisp of straw in the band of the hat for the thatcher, a crook in hand for the shepherd, hammer for the smith. Chance was someone would take you on, twelve months' labour and a ramshackle roof guaranteed. Fine for a man with a wife and youngsters to support, but not for the likes of him.

To while away a chilly night by some taproom fireside, Luke did a spot of wood carving, whittling at a chunk of wood until some recognisable shape emerged. His pack contained a selection of items for sale; spinning-tops, toy soldiers and farm animals for younger customers, and for the housewife, a choice bowl or a ladle for her shelf. His pocket being depressingly light, he was counting on some sales.

Others were bound for the same destination. There were red-cheeked country women with baskets of produce, copers with strings of ponies to trade, a goose-girl herding a rowdy gaggle of geese, as well as groups of chattering fayre-goers bent on a good day out. The more fortunate travelled in style and the road rumbled and clattered with farm-carts and gigs, fast-trotting cobs and hacks and small, soft-treading donkeys.

Luke was proudly his own man; not for him the indignity of the Hiring Fayre

At the venue, stalls and booths were set up. Somewhere a clog-dancing competition was in progress and the

Continued overleaf...

ILLUSTRATIONS: THINKSTOCK, MANDY DIXON

Luke could turn his hand to most things

Continued from previous page
rhythmic thud of nimble feet on wooden boards hammered fiercely on the air.

Luke chose his speck with care; not too close to the entrance where folks might overlook him, nor yet too far into the action where an interested party might be swept along with the general throng.

A chestnut tree promised leafy shade should the day grow hot, and he headed for this. Divesting himself of his heavy load, Luke unpacked his wares and displayed them on the ground around him. Then, settling down with his back to the tree, he waited for custom.

As always, the toys were the first to go. The wooden platter in which Luke collected his earnings was filling up pleasingly. From a nearby vendor, the smell of hot pies, rich with meat and herbs, drifted. Luke's stomach grumbled.

He was counting out coins for payment when a voice said, "What a pretty bowl."

Luke looked up into the bluest eyes he had ever seen. Hair the colour of autumn beechwoods tumbled about an elfin face. Luke's throat tightened painfully.

"Elm, that is," he said, swallowing.

She picked it up, smoothing a fingertip around the satiny rim, twisting it this way and that so she could examine the patterning of the border.

"My aunt would like this. 'Twould look well on the console table in the hallway."

She sighed. "'Sakes, it's been such a to-do since we came to the farm! Nothing but scrubbing and scouring – my hands are all but skinned with it all and we've not even started outside yet."

Luke threw the pie-vendor a glance. If he didn't hurry the pies would all be gone. He realised he was being asked the price of the bowl. "That'll be one-and-sixpence to you, my maid."

She put the item down with a little choke of regret. "Best not. I've a limited purse and my aunt trusts me not to squander it."

She gave him a smile and went on her way. Luke watched until the slight figure was swallowed up by the crowd. After which, promising a penny to a loitering urchin for keeping an eye on his gear, Luke headed for the vendor and thence to the alehouse to slake his thirst.

Inside, shoulders jostled and country voices mingled. Luke took his frothing tankard of ale outside to sit on a bench in the sunshine, and it wasn't long before he had company.

"Good day, sir. Mind if I join you?"

"Not in the least."

Luke made room for the be-whiskered fellow whose broadcloth and boots labelled him farmer.

"Grand day for the fayre," the man said, swigging his ale.

"Aye, 'tis. I'm a stranger here myself. My last billet was at Tilstock."

"You're a Shropshire man, then?"

"Not I. More like everywhere and nowhere. Yourself?"

"Oh, Cheshire born and bred am I. Name's Roland Madely, of Clegg Farm."

"Luke Tabbet."

"From everywhere and nowhere," the farmer finished with a laugh. "There's nothing wrong with being a travelling man. You get to see the world. No ties either, I suppose?"

"Exactly so. You've nice countryside hereabouts. Tidy."

The farmer's face darkened. "I wouldn't say that. Bridgend as borders my place is nothing but thistle and dock."

"Oh aye?" A thought struck. "Would the owner be looking for staff?"

"Her'll be lucky. Who'd work for a female? Don't get me wrong," Roland Madely went on hastily. "Females have their place. Take my Betsy, for example. A fine hand wi' pastry and a willing armful in bed. Dumbfounded she were, when she heard as two women had taken over Bridgend. For Betsy that's quite something."

"Two women?" A picture of speedwell-blue eyes in an elfin face rose in Luke's mind. "Would one be a dainty miss with coppery curls?"

"Correct. The aunt's a different kettle of fish entirely." The man gave an emphatic roll of his eyes. "I wouldn't care to get on the wrong side of that one. There's a lad and all, bookish sort. He'll not be much use on a farm." The farmer paused. "Why do you ask?"

"A young woman came to my… my stall." Luke had his pride. Admitting to have staked a pitch rather than trade the more purse-reducing way of hiring a

Continued overleaf...

Luke looked up into the bluest eyes he had ever seen and his throat tightened

Continued from previous page

stand would have dented his feelings sorely. He told the farmer what the girl had said to him about her aunt.

The man nodded. "Neglected, the place was when the old chap died. This one has inherited a heap of trouble. Her'd be better off selling and buying something more suited to her needs, like a cottage in the village. I've been and made an offer m'self."

"And?"

"Got told what to do with my money. Mistress Stokes isn't one to be meddling with lightly."

Luke was getting the picture. "So the lady is widowed, then?" he asked.

"Not her. Spinster, by all account, took over her deceased sister's offspring, brought them up single-handed."

"Not easy. Not that I can lay claim to experience in those matters."

The farmer looked at Luke. He saw a man perhaps in his early forties, personable, strong-faced. There was a genuine quality about him. Here was a man in whom you could put your trust.

"If you was wanting work and you don't object to a gaffer in petticoats..."

Luke thought fast. It would be steady employment. After the biting insecurity of last winter, the prospect tempted. Happen, he mused on a pinprick of alarm, he was getting a tad long in the tooth to keep moving.

"Well then, what will be, will be," he told the farmer happily. Luke was a firm believer in Fate.

By the time he was back at his pitch, he had thought again... be at the mercy of some woman who likely wouldn't know a lea of wheat from one of clover? No, not him.

By mid-afternoon he had sold the bulk of his wares. Gathering up his belongings, Luke made to leave. He had almost reached the exit when a cry rang out.

"Let go of me! Leave me be! Oh, help me, someone!"

A girl was fending off a pair of drunks. One was investigating the contents of her shopping-basket while the other was attempting to steal a kiss.

"Hey, you! Let the maid alone!"

There was a genuine quality about him; here was a man you could surely trust

Luke dropped his gear and plunged in. A brief scuffle and the troublemakers gave in and then quickly made themselves scarce.

"Thank you, sir... oh, it's you!" She managed a tremulous smile.

In silence Luke helped retrieve the scattered shopping and return it to the basket. Then, delving into his pack, he brought out the elm-wood bowl.

"I reckon this needs a home and I can't think of a better one. Take it with my good wishes."

Blue eyes met dark brown in quiet appraisal. "Luke," she began. "It is Luke, isn't it? I bumped into our neighbour. He thought you might be looking for work."

"Mebbe. Mebbe not, Miss..."

"Rose. Rose Meredith. My brother's name is William and my aunt is called Miranda Stokes. Luke,

we need a farm manager. If you could sort out our land for us and advise us about stocking it we'd be eternally grateful. My aunt will pay."

"But –"

"There's a cottage – a bit tumbledown."

"That can be dealt with."

Joy blazed on her face. "You'll come?"

"I never said that, Miss, er…"

"Just Rose. Continue along the road to the fork. Right will take you to Tarporley. Left for Bridgend." She stopped, breathless. "I'll leave it with you, then – and thank you for the bowl."

A pert smile and she was walking away. She boarded a waiting pony trap and drove off, and eventually Luke turned to retrieve his gear.

Presently he was tramping on his way, the sun now behind him, his pocket satisfactorily full and jingling. It had been a fair day at the fayre and no mistake.

At length he arrived at the fork.

To the right a milestone announced the certainty of a village inn and genial company. About to take it, Luke paused… and then, without any more hesitation, he took the other.

THE AUTHOR SAYS… "Driving down a country lane to town I saw a man trudging along with a load of hedgerow tools in a sack on his back. The story just jumped into my head. I wrote the first part in the car park at Tesco!"

Life Ahead

Just how far would you go to breathe new life into your marriage... to the end of the Universe and back?

By David J Ayres

The ice age had gone by 2207. The sea had taken vast tracts of land, so that new land had to be reclaimed from the waves. The population was small, reduced by superbug infections and several global bird 'flu pandemics.

Jasper had always known that serious money could be made from land reclamation and that is precisely how he had become exceedingly rich. His company, New Atlantis, specialised in creating polders in the Dutch style, enclosing areas of the sea bed, draining them, drying them and planting them.

From the window of his spacious office, he gazed across Dogger Bank, a sweeping stretch of green parkland, receding into the distance towards Belgium.

"It could save our marriage, Jas."

"Yes, it could but it will also decimate our bank accounts."

He turned to Tanya, in her thirties as he was, and took in the sleek, sophisticated woman, poised and alert in the leather chair by his desk.

Why was their marriage failing? Could it still be salvaged?

Tanya looked back at him, the pale spring sunshine gilding her beige suit and setting her long auburn hair ablaze.

Jasper scratched his head and gazed at his long shadow which fell across the big rosewood desktop.

"If we do this thing, Tanya, we'll be away for a couple of years and several billion worse off."

"Yes, but it would be the greatest adventure of all time and it would make or break us as a couple. We would either have to get along together or we would kill each other in the process."

ILLUSTRATIONS: THINKSTOCK, MANDY DIXON

She was searching his dark, handsome face as she spoke and wondering why this man had gradually become a stranger to her. This meeting with Jasper was as close as they had been for several days.

"You realise you and I built our fortune in the land reclamation business and not in the exploration of interstellar space?"

He smiled at her and came forward to sit on the desk.

"Realistically, Jas, what are we going to do with our money? We chose to have no children and we already have all we need."

She reached to touch his leg but he rose, shoved his hands in his pockets and began to pace up and down. She knew better than to interrupt, so she waited.

Jasper said, "Check to see if we can use that old derelict site in Florida. It's called Cape Canaveral. I'll sort out a planning and production team. We'll need something with a sub-space drive and it will be eye-wateringly expensive."

Tanya saw him warming to the scheme. It seemed ages since she had seen him so animated. She knew this was a good idea.

Tanya and Jasper stepped off the shuttle together. From London to Orlando, Florida, was just a twenty minute trip and Jasper had hardly stopped talking, his eyes bright with the old enthusiasm she remembered.

Tanya searched her husband's face and wondered how he'd become a stranger

At length he spun on his heel towards her and grinned a boyish grin.

"Let's do it, Tan. No-one else is doing it. The Earth Space Agency has this scandal going on about funding and the Chinese are too preoccupied with their base on Europa."

Tanya leaned forward. She was grinning too.

Although the sky was grey and the heat was clammy, Jasper continued to talk without pausing all the way to the desolate site of Cape Canaveral.

As the dust stirred up by the hovertaxi settled around them, they made their way towards the old mission control building. Only a dozen private vehicles were

Continued overleaf...

Continued from previous page
parked outside, so most of the team had either come by monorail or hovertaxi.

"Do you have your notes, Jas?" Tanya panted, smiling at him and tasting salty sweat on her upper lip.

"They're here," he brandished them at her with a laugh, "Although I don't need them. I know exactly what I need to say. Project Darwin starts here."

She was having to trot to keep up with him. It was just like the old days, before they were rich, before they slept in separate beds.

There were over a hundred people in the huge room which had been mission control so many years ago. Now stripped of all its equipment, the echoing hall contained about a hundred and fifty chairs, a table with a few more chairs and a base for a hologram display. Men and women of all ages and nationalities stood in groups talking.

When Tanya and Jasper swept in from a door at the front of the building, a hush fell upon the assembly and all eyes turned towards them.

Tanya sat watching Jasper open the meeting, his easy, conversational manner quickly charming his audience. As she watched him, she understood why she had first fallen in love with this man and struggled to comprehend how she had let him begin to slip through her fingers.

The brilliantly colourful hologram displays rotated around him and expanded towards the high ceiling, star systems, planetary systems and galaxies. The proposed Darwin vehicle raised a gasp from the spectators as it hovered between Jasper and the front row of chairs; a massive, gleaming thing that was almost impossibly beautiful.

Tanya realised that the eyes were all turning towards her now. Jasper raised his arm behind him to beckon her to come forward.

As she left her seat he said, "Ladies and gentlemen, this gorgeous apparition before you which makes even the Darwin vehicle look commonplace is my wife, Tanya. She will take up the arrangements from here."

Tanya stepped before the audience to an unexpectedly loud burst of applause. The husband and wife team, she thought. This is what I wanted. The stars and the galaxies can go to hell.

By the time dusk came to Cape Canaveral, the plans were laid and further meetings were diaried. As they travelled back to London on the last shuttle of the evening, they both knew Project Darwin was a reality.

It was a little more than three years after that meeting that the Darwin found itself heading towards the Andromeda Galaxy.

Its complement of sixty-three people, headed, in a democratic way, by Jasper and Tanya, got along well and processed reams of data as the time slid by, without day or night and without seasons.

On board was the most sophisticated probing and sensor equipment ever devised. There was plenty to probe. The Milky Way has four hundred billion stars

in a spiral disc shape, like a whirlpool. From the outer edge of the galaxy to the black hole in its centre is fifty thousand light years. Even taking into account the gigantic speed of the Darwin, a distance like that takes many weeks.

"Well, Tan, we're on schedule and we have a happy team." Jasper squeezed her wrist and she turned to look up at him.

"Disappointing though, that we've found so little yet. Perhaps we'll have better luck in the Andromeda Galaxy."

They had probed and investigated billions of stars and planetary systems very much like our own. Their mission – to discover and investigate other forms of life – was half complete. They had quartered the Milky Way and had found only simple life – algae and lichen. There was very little water anywhere and much of that was frozen. Most of the ice they had found had turned out to be "dry ice"; frozen carbon dioxide.

The team were puzzled but reserved judgment as they hurtled towards the Andromeda Galaxy, two and a half million light years away.

In the comfortably appointed rest room Tanya and Jasper sat together on a broad, plump sofa. The rest of the team milled around them, giving the impression of a busy airport departure lounge. As their coffees went cold on the table beside them, they talked quietly.

"You've been stuck with me on the Darwin for a year now, Jas. Do you feel you want to kill me yet?"

"No chance. Too many witnesses."

She slapped him playfully on the arm.

"Anyway, I must go," she said, "I've work to do. We have to tie up all the loose ends before we get to Andromeda."

"OK, Tan, see you later. Incidentally I'll sleep here tonight while the maintenance team repair the ceiling in my cabin."

Tanya stopped in mid-stride and turned to him, "You can always come to my cabin – if you want to, that is. I mean if you'd rather..."

Jasper cleared his throat, "Yes, fine, thank you, I'd like that."

Tanya coloured as she walked away.

While the second shift, known as the night shift, took over the various stations on board, Tanya and Jasper began to rediscover each other in the darkness of Tanya's cabin. Eventually they lost themselves in sleep, floating further away than even the Andromeda Galaxy.

As she watched him she understood why she had first fallen in love with this man

Andromeda yielded the same and the atmosphere inside the Darwin became subdued. The team could scarcely believe the results of this most exhaustive search for extra-terrestrial life ever attempted. What life there was,

Continued overleaf...

Continued from previous page
appeared to be rudimentary, mainly single cell – until just before the point of no return...

On the very day that the Darwin had to turn back towards Earth, carbon emissions were detected from a small planet many light years away from them.

The Darwin team established that it was not a forest fire, although that in itself would have been astonishing. These were cooking fires. Animal flesh was being cooked.

Morale soared.

Later, lying in the pitch darkness in Tanya's bed, Jasper whispered, "We're going to have to come back, Tan. We need a second expedition here."

"This has all made me realise just how special our little blue planet is."

Jasper reached across to her and began stroking her hair.

"It's a hell of a responsibility being us, Tan. This trip will change history. This is bigger than Christopher Columbus."

Tanya lay back and luxuriated in his touch, "I'm so proud of us, Jas." She nestled against the crook of his arm.

"Now we put the data into cogent form and transmit the whole lot back to Earth. I don't think we'll have any trouble funding the next expedition."

Tanya said, "We've got an hour before the news conference with Darwin base back at Cape Canaveral. It seems the news media of the entire planet will be gathered there. There'll be a delay between question and answer but we're close enough for it to be minimal."

Cape Canaveral was hot and humid. When the door of the Darwin Centre slid silently aside, hordes of media people pushed their way inside. When they were all seated around the hologram platform, inside the big auditorium, there was an almost reverential hush.

Then the two wraith-like figures of Jasper and Tanya appeared before them, flickering and buzzing, because they were still at extreme range.

Addressing the two figures in the hologram, a reporter asked, "So you've discovered life?"

Jasper replied, "Yes, but only simple life – except for an Earth-size planet at the extreme edge of the Andromeda Galaxy. We're pretty sure there are people there, using fire to cook."

"So we're not alone?" the man persisted.

The flickering image of Tanya turned to him, smiling, and said, "No, we are not alone. But we will need to reach out across the emptiness of space to make contact with others."

As if echoing this sentiment, Tanya reached for Jasper's hand and squeezed it firmly. Jasper turned to her, realising that he too had crossed empty space and found his own life.

Fancy That!

Fascinating **Summer flower** facts!

◆ The Californian Poppy has been the state flower of California since 1890.

◆ **There are more than 270,000 species of flower in the world.**

◆ The daisy was originally known as the "day's eye" because it resembled the sun.

◆ **A clump of nettles can house up to five species of caterpillar during the course of a summer.**

◆ Planting parsley in a garden encourages bees.

The yellow water lily is nicknamed the brandy bottle

◆ **A flower frog is a metal device that fits in a vase to hold the stems in an arrangement.**

The larkspur is the birth flower of people born in July

◆ Britain's first fields and meadows were created by Stone Age people 6000 years ago.

◆ **According to folklore, picking foxgloves will offend the fairies.**

The carnation is the UK's bestselling cut flower

Poppies can grow up to 4ft tall and 6 inches across

◆ **The White House employs a Chief Floral Designer and four assistants to help the First Lady plan arrangements throughout the presidential residence.**

◆ The Titan Arum is the world's loftiest flower, standing 3 metres tall. It's also the world's foulest smelling!

The Purple Waistcoat

Of five sisters, only two now remained to endure their mother's matchmaking. Yet this time might be different...

By Pauline Saull

lizabeth dreaded her mother's boring afternoon teas. They were, she knew, only an excuse for her dear parent to invite every available unmarried young man to the house in the hope they would fall for her daughters.

Though over the past three years, she had to admit, they'd been pretty successful. First Anna, then Sara had been snapped up – and finally three months ago the prettiest sister, Emma, had married a lawyer from London. Now, there remained only Elizabeth and her youngest sister Katherine.

The two girls were both out of sorts as they prepared for what they considered yet another afternoon of tedium.

"Why, Mama, must we do this?" Elizabeth protested. "I feel like a prize animal being brought out for inspection."

Her mother's lips tightened. "Don't speak in such an unseemly manner, Elizabeth. It is no such thing. Papa and I are only thinking of your future. A good marriage is imperative for girls today, and while Katherine is still young, you..."

"I am twenty-five, Mama, not quite the old maid yet. Perhaps they will ask to see our teeth," she muttered.

"What was that?"

"Nothing, Mama."

"Well in any case, today will be different. The two young men coming here this afternoon are high-ranking officers on leave for a time before their return to Southern Africa. So put on your best dresses, girls, and Elizabeth, take the pout off your mouth."

Katherine waited until their mother had left the room. She began twisting her thick red hair into a plait, a thoughtful look on her face.

"I'm not quite the old maid yet. Perhaps they will ask to see our teeth," she said

"South Africa," she mused. "I quite like the idea of that. Picture the freedom."

Elizabeth stared at her sister's reflection in the oval mirror. "You'd marry just to get away?"

"Of course."

Continued overleaf...

PICTURES: MANDY DIXON, THINKSTOCK

Continued from previous page

"But what about love?"

"Love," Katherine scoffed, "is not for me. It makes fools and slaves of women."

Elizabeth studied her own serious, unremarkable face. The clear grey eyes, her one redeeming feature, stared back at her. "Well I shall only marry for love," she declared. "Nothing less will do. I would rather remain a spinster."

Secretly, she thought that was probably what would happen. The eldest and plainest of five sisters in any family was usually doomed for spinsterhood; the chance of love coming her way now – four months away from her twenty-sixth birthday – was slender to say the least.

The bell rang in the bedroom.

"We're summoned. Come, let's get it over with." Elizabeth smoothed her dress down and took Katherine's hand, leading her out along the landing. On their way downstairs they stopped on hearing the sound of unmistakable – and to them, seldom heard – deep, male, abandoned laughter.

"Well!" Katherine pulled her plait forward onto her shoulder and pinched her cheeks. "This may be more interesting than I at first thought, sister dear."

In the drawing room a well-stacked fire snapped and crackled in the grate. Seated on either side of it was a young man, both standing immediately the girls entered.

Their mother drew them forward. "Major Moreland, Lieutenant Capper. These are my daughters, Elizabeth and Katherine. Please be seated, gentlemen. Tea is on the way."

"After you, ladies." With a charming smile Major Moreland pulled out two chairs.

"Well, well," Katherine said later, fanning herself. "What did you make of them?"

The two girls had retired to their room, but sleep was the last thing on Elizabeth's mind. She was in turmoil.

Robert, Robert, Major Robert Moreland.

She wanted to say his name out loud, speak of his beautiful dark velvety eyes, his thick russet hair and that quite beautiful smile, but could not.

"I … I found both men extremely polite," she said.

"Polite? Goodness gracious, Elizabeth! Lieutenant Capper – Daniel – is entirely scrumptious. He whispered that he wishes to see me again and I agreed." Katherine sighed. "And did you not think his blue eyes divine? I do declare, I fear I am a little in love already!"

"In love?" Elizabeth's hand went to her throat. "What makes you of all people mention the word?"

"Elizabeth –" Katherine turned to face her sister. "Is it not true that neither of us have ever met such dashing gentlemen before?" She didn't wait for an answer.

"Nor such interesting and amusing ones. No wonder I previously scorned the idea of love, but now –" her eyes took on a dreamy look – "I quite like the notion." She giggled. "Though I'm sorry to leave you with the dandy, dearest sister."

"A dandy?" Elizabeth bridled. "Whatever makes you say that?"

Katherine shrugged. "Only a dandy, a *fop*, would wear such an atrociously coloured waistcoat. Did you see Mama's lip curl when his coat parted to reveal it?"

Elizabeth smiled and began pulling the pins from her hair, running her fingers through the rich brown tresses, her grey eyes glowing with suppressed happiness – for Robert's choice of waistcoat had meant something entirely different to her.

It showed him to be a man who gave not a tinker's toss for convention, one who dressed freely to suit himself instead of pleasing others, which Elizabeth found very appealing.

All my adult life, she thought, *I have without knowing it been waiting for just such a man; one who will be kind, thoughtful, caring, and... different. Yes, he's different – and he makes my heart beat faster.*

Oh, I cannot wait to see him again!

Katherine had clambered into bed. Elizabeth picked up her hairbrush.

"Come, sister," Katherine urged. "Let us put out the lantern and whisper."

Elizabeth smiled. "Two more minutes," she promised.

Her thoughts swung back to Robert. As he'd been leaving, and while Mama was occupied keeping an eye on Katherine flirting with the young Lieutenant, she had expressed her admiration for the beauty of his purple satin waistcoat.

He'd smiled. "I'm glad you approve. I adore it. It was made by a very clever seamstress, a Zulu woman in South Africa." He whispered close to her ear, "A place I would dearly love to show you one day. It has wonderful weather; imagine, Elizabeth always being warmed by eternal sunshine, constant blue skies, vast open spaces... it would be a fine place to live and start a family."

Elizabeth's pulse rate had quickened with excitement at his words. "You would consider such a move?"

Robert's dark eyes looked steadily into hers. "With the right woman by my side I could live anywhere – but South Africa, yes." He smiled. "Here comes your Mama. May I call on you again tomorrow, Elizabeth?"

Quickly she'd reached to run her finger down the smooth purple cloth of his waistcoat.

"Only if you promise to wear this. I adore it too."

Robert caught that finger and raised it briefly to his lips. "I promise," he said.

"Imagine always being warmed by eternal sunshine – vast open spaces"

THE AUTHOR SAYS... **"*The Purple Waistcoat* was inspired by a writing group I attend. Each week three or four words are picked out of an envelope and we write a short story about those words. It's a challenge I enjoy."**

The Road to Morecambe

How will Mike and Andy, neighbours and political enemies, survive a seventy-mile walk in each other's company?

By Alison Carter

If you're going to walk seventy miles in three and a half days, and one of you has got a new hip, and the other's more deaf than he admits, you ought to start out on good terms.

Mike and Andy were planning such a walk. The map was laid out on Mike and Christine's kitchen table. Andy was tracing the route with a finger, frowning.

"The important thing," said Mike, "so my surgeon says, is to keep moving. They used to recommend rest with a new hip, but that's all old hat."

"I suppose I'll take my Altrincham one," said Andy vaguely. "Although it could be warm."

"Your Altrincham what?" Mike stared at the back of Andy's balding head.

"Hat." Andy straightened up. "Or my Stetson. Are you bringing a hat?"

"I was talking about my hip," said Mike. "You ought to wear your hearing aid."

"I don't need the hearing aid," Andy said. "It's a walk. I'll be using my legs."

"No, I mean – Oh, never mind."

"I can't be doing with artificial aids," Andy said.

"I hope you're not casting aspersions on my new hip," Mike said tartly. "It's pure technology, my –"

"I never hear the last of your hip." Andy began folding up the map.

"Hear the last?" Mike sighed and looked at the map. "You don't hear the beginning."

"I told you." Andy shook his head pityingly. "The beginning is the top of our street, six am, Wednesday fortnight. We'll be in Morecambe in time for kick-off."

There was a short scuffle and the map tore, separating Urmston and Stretford

Andy began to fold the map, badly. Mike tried to take over. There was a short scuffle and the map tore, separating Urmston and Stretford for ever.

Mike and Andy were next-door neighbours. Mike was an ex-accountant of seventy-two who liked cricket and voted Conservative. Andy was a semi-retired estate agent, an ardent fan of

Continued overleaf...

ILLUSTRATIONS: MANDY MURRAY, THINKSTOCK

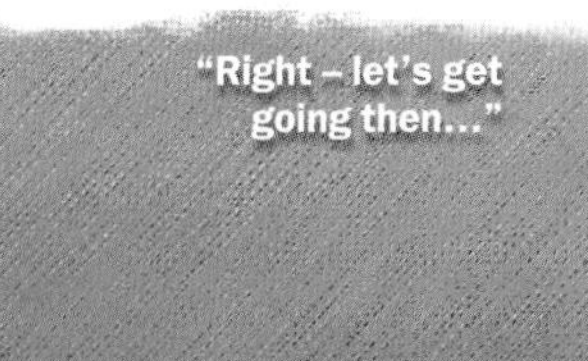
"Right – let's get
going then..."

Continued from previous page

Altrincham FC and a Labour man for all his fifty-nine years.

Mike was small and wiry. "I can still wear my school blazer," he often said proudly.

Andy was five inches taller but ten inches larger about the waist.

"I don't have a school blazer," he said. "I didn't go to a toffee-nosed school."

They often commented that they only maintained an acquaintance because their wives were such good friends. And, as Andy observed one summer day from his side of the laurel hedge, "it's never wise to get on the wrong side of the other side of a semi."

"What are you going on about?" Mike called back.

"I said," Andy replied, "it's never wise… oh, never mind. Is your hearing going?"

The plan for the walk was hatched one evening in the Railway Arms. The two men went once a week on a Sunday, to put each other right politically.

"The Club needs a boost," Andy said, setting down two brimming glasses. "Financially and … spiritually."

"Which club would that be?" Mike asked politely, as if he didn't know.

Andy ignored the comment. Or he didn't hear it – you never could tell.

"I'm thinking of a walk, a really long one. We're playing Morecambe away on the Saturday afternoon, so I'll have a sort of a… goal." He paused. "Goal. That was quite good, wasn't it?"

"I didn't think you were familiar with goals, at Altrincham FC," said Mike.

"Very funny." Andy sniffed. "It's seventy miles. I can probably do it in three and a half days. I'll get sponsors, and of course the publicity."

There was a pause. Mike picked up his glass. "I may as well come."

Andy frowned. "It's a nice offer, Mike, but you've a good few years on me. And with the new hip and everything…"

Mike put down his glass.

"I have exercised every day of my life," he said. "It was part of my all-round education. I can walk as far as a man half my age. Did you know that I can still wear my school –"

"Yes I did," said Andy quickly.

"Well, I could walk from here to Morecambe just as well as you." Mike said as he looked pointedly at his neighbour's midriff. "As long as I don't have to bother with the match at the end. As you know, I'm more a cricketing man."

"I hope I don't repeat myself that much when I'm seventy-two."

"Sorry?"

"I'm the one with the hearing aid," said Andy. "I've put the idea to the lads in the supporters' club, actually."

"Any volunteers?"

"Give them time," Andy said. "There's a lot of younger men – working full-time, young kids. Lots to arrange."

"So, nobody then. Well, if you don't want me along –"

"Did I say that? No, more the merrier. Chris and Di will be delighted. They'd like us to be more… co-operative."

"Fat chance." Mike sipped his beer.

"Chalk and cheese," declared Andy, with satisfaction.

"I didn't think you were familiar with goals, at Altrincham FC," said Mike

Mike strode into the Post Office

The chairman of the Club was there to see them off on a chilly morning, plus a girl from the local paper who looked as if she'd rather be asleep.

"Good luck, gentlemen," the chairman said warmly.

"I'm just along to exercise my new hip," said Mike, tapping his leg firmly.

The chairman looked confused. "Well," he said, "good of you to accompany Andy here. The Club's very grateful."

"I'm not a football man," said Mike. "Cricket's my –"

"Let's go," said Andy firmly, and strode away. Mike hurried after him and overtook. They both vanished round a corner.

Mike was remarkably fit for his age and kept up a good pace. Andy's longer legs meant he could outstrip Mike when he pushed himself. They were so competitive that one was generally fifty yards ahead, aiming to get to the next village first and find someone to impress.

Just outside Leigh, Mike strode into a Post Office and leaned against the counter, breathing hard to show the effort he'd been making.

"We're just walking," he said casually, "from Altrincham to Morecambe."

Andy was hard on his heels. "In aid of Altrincham Football Club," he said loudly.

The postmistress looked politely interested.

"Except that I'm just along for fitness," Mike put in. "And to keep an eye on Andy here, my more ample neighbour."

Mike spent a lot of time on his mobile phone. He made calls to everyone he could think of about his progress.

"You can't live without that thing, can you?" said Andy as they walked along a towpath, rucksacks rising and falling with each step.

Mike tucked the phone back into what he called his security wallet and Andy insisted on referring to as his bum bag. "It's a brilliant invention," he said. "Provides regular stimulating conversation."

"Right. And my conversation isn't stimulating enough?"

"It's opinionated enough." Mike increased his pace. "Take ID cards, for instance."

"No, don't go there again, for Heaven's sake," Andy said pleadingly. They heaved open a gate and tramped through. Andy muttered as he pulled it shut, "Mobiles. Invasion of privacy."

"Don't be ridiculous. It's only because you can't hear what people are saying half the time."

"No, it's a matter of principle. I'd go so far as to say it's a human rights issue."

"Pinko liberal."

"Old fogey."

It started to rain.

Continued overleaf...

Continued from previous page

At each stop, Andy talked to everybody who would listen (and quite a few who wouldn't) about the Club. Mike talked about his new hip and his astonishing fitness, for a seventy-two-year-old. They bickered over the best place for a cup of tea, about the merits of waterproof trousers, whether a Full English Breakfast slows you down, about who was the finest British Prime Minister of the twentieth century.

The second night, they had a row about genetic engineering in their motel lounge and the owner asked if they could keep the noise down.

"I've a group of lads here on a stag weekend," she explained apologetically, "who say can they have some peace and quiet, please?"

It was a fine Saturday morning when Mike and Andy set out on the last leg. They were both grumpy. After four miles Mike held up the plastic-covered map and called back over his shoulder, "We can take the canal and approach Lancaster from the south, or be boring and go up the A6."

"You what?" Andy shouted.

"The A6," called Mike.

Andy caught up. "Basics?" He raised his eyes to heaven. "If you're going to start on again about Back to Basics, when I'm almost there, then I'm just going to call a taxi on that mobile of yours."

"I just said, canal path or A6?"

"Take the A6? On a lovely day like this? Don't be silly. That would be boring."

Mike sighed. He looked along the main road they had to cross. "I'm not going all that way round to reach that footbridge," he said, and began to climb the metal fence that edged the road.

"Always finding a way to be awkward,"

"He needs t[...] there for kick-[...]

grumbled Andy. "And dangerous."

Mike was already bringing his second leg over the fence. He winced suddenly.

Andy had noticed the previous evening that he'd seemed stiff, getting up from his chair to stomp off to bed after their latest "discussion". The scene seemed to go into slow-motion as Mike's booted foot caught in the gap between two bars, and his supporting hand was yanked from the fence by the unbalancing of his weight. Andy threw himself towards the fence but Mike was down, an arm crumpling under him as he landed with a sickening thud on the dusty verge.

There were very few words during the following minutes. Andy worked so quickly that Mike, even through his pain, was astonished. Andy checked for other injuries, talking quietly – half to himself, half getting Mike to confirm something. He moved Mike's legs away from the road and sat him up, very gently. He used the contents of his rucksack to keep Mike's now oddly-shaped arm immobile.

"Before you take the Mickey," he muttered, "no, I wasn't a Boy Scout. My firm sent me on a course. Maybe they knew I'd wind up sixty-five miles from home with an old bloke who's had a fight with a fence."

He found Mike's mobile. "They have their uses," he said gruffly as he jabbed at the buttons.

Mike could tell he'd got a dial tone. "Nine nine nine, I should think," he said weakly. "Sorry."

Andy nodded, concentrating. "Just wish I wasn't so damned deaf."

Mike looked into the younger man's anxious face and didn't point out that it was the first time he'd admitted he was hard of hearing.

They sat side by side for fifteen minutes, Andy wrapping more and more of his own clothes round Mike's shoulders, checking the position of his arm, asking how he felt. Mike was pale.

"Another two minutes and I'm going to splint it," Andy said quietly. "So take a deep breath, mate."

But then they heard the wail of the siren.

"And you, sir –" The paramedic turned to Andy, when the first flurry of activity was over and Mike was ready for the off. "Well done for your prompt reporting. Did you come across Mike here while you were out walking?"

Andy looked up at Mike, propped up inside the ambulance, then away again.

"Actually we're togeth – He's…"

He coughed. "He's, um, a friend."

Mike looked up in surprise from where he sat stooped on the narrow bed.

"Good," the paramedic said briskly. "So you'll come along? I'm Kev, by the way."

"No." Mike held up his good arm weakly. "He needs to get to the Morecambe ground, for kick-off. That's why we're here. It's important."

Andy shook his head.

"It's only football," he said quickly. "Look, er, Kev, will it mend, his arm?"

Kev surveyed the injury. "I've every reason to say yes. But you're not our youngest ever patient, Mike, so it might take –"

"He's fit as a fiddle," interrupted Andy fervently. "He's just walked here from Altrincham. Seventy miles, near enough."

"Blimey," said Kev, as his colleague returned and motioned that they should be off. Andy, laden with rucksacks and clothes, followed them round the vehicle.

"Do you know, Mike here can still fit into his school blazer?"

"Can he?" Kev was concentrating on the task ahead.

"We've been neighbours for ten years. Seems like no time. He's a fine –"

But Andy's voice was drowned by the siren and the noise of the engine.

"Another two minutes and I'm going to splint it. So take a deep breath, mate"

THE AUTHOR SAYS…

"We were amazed when my dad planned a marathon fundraising walk with his neighbour. They are the proverbial chalk and cheese. But nobody (as they say) died."

Say It With Flowers!

We all know that red roses symbolise love. But did you know that every other flower has a meaning, too? Victorian lovers invented a code in which they could have secret conversations by exchanging small posies known as tussie mussies.

Hydrangea
"You are heartless."

Carnations

Yellow "You have disappointed me"

Striped "Sorry I can't be with you"

White Innocence and faithfulness

Pink A mother's love

White heather
"Good luck."

Peach blossom
"I am your captive."

Iris
"Good news."

Poinsettia
"Be of good cheer"

Primrose "I can't live without you."

Sweetpea "Thank you."

Monkshood "Beware, a deadly foe is near."

Pansy "Think of me"

Love in a Mist "You puzzle me."

Rhododendron "Beware, I am dangerous."

Yellow lily "I'm walking on air."

Yellow tulip "There's sunshine in your smile."

Roses

Red True love

Dried white Sorrow

Dark pink Gratitude

Violet Love at first sight

WORDS: DOUGLAS MCPHERSON PICTURES: ALAMY, SHUTTERSTOCK, THINKSTOCK

Echo Beach

Life says it cannot be and we have to move on... but after forty years of living apart, can true young love still survive?

By Sarah England

By the time his email arrived I'd been on my own for a while. I stared. *Billy Tate.*

Even as I was clicking on the new message, the rational side of my brain kicked in: there must be lots of Billy Tates... it was spam... coincidence... something to do with my career as an illustrator...

But my heart knew better.

Billy Tate.

As his brief message leapt from the screen, I was sixteen again in an instant.

Silently, I mouthed, *Hi Billy!*

My eyes stinging hotly as I read... *Is this Kim Beecham? The same Kim I used to know a long, long time ago? You'll know if I say, 'Hello Echo!' Sincere apologies if I have the wrong lady.*

Immediately I started to type, as my heart raced and my fingers flew across the keyboard with a mind of their own.

Billy! I think this might be what's known these days as an OMG moment! How are you? Where are you?

I sat back.

Thing was, when Billy and I last saw each other, I'd been on the back seat of my dad's car being driven home in disgrace, and he'd been in the rear-view mirror... angrily kick-starting his motorbike. Our passion had been way too passionate – Billy having left school to start work on a building site but rarely turning up, and me still at school taking O Levels.

When we met it was in the local pub, where I wasn't supposed to be. *Echo Beach* was playing on the jukebox, and he and his mates were planning a round-Europe trip on their bikes.

He made his move and I was captivated by his coal-black hair, his soft, hazel eyes, and the way his gaze seemed to melt when he looked at me. I loved him instantly. Wildly.

I guess it was the wild bit my parents worried about. It's when the door-slamming started at home. The shouting matches, the threats of being locked in my room, and marched to the school gates and back. Then they didn't believe a word I said. Everything changed.

So Billy and I did what thousands of teenagers had done before – we ran off

So naturally, Billy and I did what thousands of teenagers had done before us – we ran off. Me skittering down the drainpipe clutching a holdall, Billy

Continued overleaf...

PICTURES: MANDY MURRAY, THINKSTOCK

I remembered
him as he
was then

Continued from previous page

pushing his motorbike stealthily as a cat, to the end of the road, past the closed curtains of suburbia, and out onto the glittering highway, powering us both away into the darkness.

By the time they tracked us down we'd run out of cash and I was working as a waitress in a Bar & Grill.

I think that was probably the defining moment of my young life – being removed by the elbow from the premises by my granite-faced father. I should thank him. I got my A Levels and studied fine art at university, married and had two wonderful children.

And yet…Dear God, how my raw heart ached. Sinking onto the cold linoleum of the bathroom floor when we hit home three hours later. Wracked with mind-numbing sobs.

Picking up the pieces had taken time.

Yet here I was, a middle-aged woman with her heart still catapulting at the sight of his name. I tried to type some more but the right words wouldn't come.

Forty years had passed. He wouldn't be the same sinewy, intense, mean and moody teenager I'd adored. He'd be

Where had he gone on his motorbike that fateful day?

nearly sixty. With what kind of a life behind him? Did he have children – or grandchildren?

In the end I stuck to the initial lines I'd chosen and hoped he'd answer.

Two months later we met. After what grew into an almost daily correspondence, I looked forward to opening my emails. I enjoyed the catch-ups and the photo exchanges.

"We're shocked, aren't we?" I said.

He laughed, ambled towards me, pulled me into his chest with one of those great bear hugs I used to crave.

Later, many hours and several stiff drinks later, we took a walk down the tree-lined promenade and he reached for my hand, clasping it gently at first, then rather more tightly. Like all these decades hadn't passed at all, and I was

Forty years had passed; he wouldn't be the sinewy, moody teenager I'd adored

Nothing recent, though, I noticed. The snapshots he sent were mostly of his children and grandchildren. A few holiday pics… and the only one he had of me was taken on my daughter's wedding day seven years ago – most of my face covered with a hat.

So it was a shock.

We'd decided on a small Tudor hotel in the middle of our home town. A creakily dark, comfortable bar we both knew well. I recognised him straight away. Yet still my mouth hung open at the lack of hair, the paunch, the crinkly eyes… though still as warm as melting caramel… staring at me.

Suddenly conscious of how I must look to him, with my now somewhat matronly figure and preference for comfortable shoes, I felt the heat travelling up my neck into my face.

still his girl – only all over again.

Oh, we'd had full lives, happy lives. We were older, chubbier, wiser and more pragmatic. And yet, funny business, time, isn't it? We move through it and yet we stay the same. The same tingles running up my spine. The same softening look in his eyes as he stopped and turned to me.

Love, I think it's called. Some things simply don't change at all.

THE AUTHOR SAYS… "A long-lost friend recently got in touch with me by email after 30 years had passed. It would never have happened without the internet and I wondered how it might work with an old flame…"

Sent From Heaven

Jack had promised to win them a holiday to Paris – but what were the chances? And now she was all alone

By Christine Sutton

Hearing the letterbox clunk, Vera hurried into the hallway. Lying on the mat were two long white envelopes. Was it possible, she wondered – could Jack really have pulled it off?

Scooping them up, she tore open the first. Inside was a Ruby Wedding Anniversary card, with a picture of an elderly couple walking by the sea.

To my darling Mum on your special day. Dad almost made it, didn't he? Thinking of you. Love always, Jen.

Vera swallowed hard, fighting back tears. Today was for remembering, not for crying. Turning to the second one, she peeled open the flap.

On their last anniversary Jack had vowed that by hook or by crook, this year, their fortieth, he would take her to the most romantic city in the world, Paris. When she'd asked how he imagined they could possibly afford it, he'd cheerfully explained that he intended to win the trip and, to that end, had taken out a subscription to a competitors' magazine, *Winning Ways.*

It seemed a very hit and miss method to Vera but, sure enough, two weeks later he did actually win a prize – a T-shirt with *I'm Crackers for Camembert* on the front. The fact that neither of them actually ate Camembert was neither here nor there; at least it demonstrated it could be done.

Next to arrive was a silver photo frame, followed soon after by a magnum of champagne. Last, and most definitely least, came a Dumbo baseball cap, complete with rubber trunk and jumbo-sized ears. Smiling at the memory of Jack galumphing around the lounge, huge ears flapping like sails, Vera eased out the single folded sheet.

She had to smile at the memory of Jack galumphing round, jumbo ears flapping

Congratulations, she read, *you are one of five runners-up in our Two Cities Competition.*

Her heart rose in fleeting expectation, then sank again. Only a runner-up, not the outright winner.

ILLUSTRATIONS: THINKSTOCK, MANDY DIXON

It seemed Vera was destined never to see Paris

His prize, a copy of Charles Dickens' *A Tale of Two Cities,* would be delivered shortly, but it was the top prize Jack had been after; a trip for two to Disneyland Paris. OK, the children's theme park wasn't quite as romantic as Montmartre or the Champs-Elysées but as a base from which to visit those other places, it was ideal. To win, he'd had to complete the

Continued overleaf...

Continued from previous page
phrase *I think Dickens would enjoy Disneyland because…*

After thinking long and hard he'd settled on *Where strangely-named characters freely roam, Dickens should feel right at home!*

Kissing the envelope for luck, he'd popped it in the postbox, convinced this was the one that would get them their dream break.

Days later, he was gone. Entering the lounge one afternoon she'd found him slumped in the armchair, his skin the colour of the clouds that had driven him in from the garden. All her fervent bargaining with the Almighty had come to nothing and he'd slipped away before they even reached the hospital.

For months Vera had struggled to come to terms with her loss. The silliest things would set her off; a cuff-link rattling up the vacuum cleaner, a silver-grey hair in the comb. Even now, almost a year on, she still found it hard to accept that the love of her life was no more.

Opening Jack's comping folder to file the letter away, she was surprised to see the entry form sitting right on top. She heaved a regretful sigh. It wasn't that she would have actually *gone* to Paris on her own; she'd just wanted the pleasure of knowing that, had he lived, they would

have done so together. She was about to close the folder when she spotted the latest issue of *Winning Ways*. She'd been putting each month's issue away, unopened, in the file but now was curious to see what was inside.

She tore off the plastic wrapping and as she flicked through the pages, her eyes grew wide. Some of the prizes were amazing. Cars, caravans – even a house.

The smaller ones weren't to be sneezed at, either. At her age she might have little use for a jar of Blissful Bottoms nappy cream, and Dragon's Breath pepper sauce sounded a bit fierce, but if buying them might win her a fridge-freezer or a widescreen TV she'd find room for them in her trolley.

She closed the magazine with a snap. She was going shopping… for qualifiers.

Stepping out of the front door, Vera was struck by the state of her lawn. Living near a school was lovely, but the downside was a daily stream of sweet wrappers and crisp packets coming over the wall. Deciding it could wait until her return, she headed for the supermarket.

It didn't take long to locate the entry forms. Selecting three with prizes that appealed the most, she scanned the rules. Each required a different qualifier; the sleeve from a microwave lasagne, the label from a jar of apple sauce, and a token from a pack of teacakes. In addition, each needed a receipt. This comping lark was more complicated than it appeared.

The girl on the till watched Vera load her purchases onto the conveyer, placing dividers between each.

"You want to buy them all separate?" she asked, with heavy disdain.

"Yes, please. Sorry," Vera said meekly.

By the time she'd fished in her purse for a third time it wasn't just the girl who'd had enough; the customers behind her in the queue were starting to grumble too. Gabbling apologies, she grabbed her bags and hurried from the store.

Walking home, her thoughts turned again to the litter-strewn lawn. She wouldn't be able to relax until it had been dealt with, so after dumping her bags on the kitchen table she took an empty carrier and went back outside.

She had just finished clearing up when a wrapper came sailing over the wall

As she scooped up the sticky, insect-covered mess she found herself wishing that one day she might actually catch one of the little devils in the act. They'd think twice about doing it again once she'd finished with them, that was for sure.

Finally, she sat back, satisfied that not a scrap of rubbish remained. She was just reaching for the bag when a chocolate wrapper came sailing over the wall and landed in her lap.

Vera stared in disbelief at this new blot on her landscape before scrambling furiously to her feet. She was preparing to throw it back into the surprised face of the "schoolboy" who'd tossed it when she

Continued overleaf...

Continued from previous page

found herself staring at a bald, muscular youth with more tattoos than skin.

"You, umm, seem to have dropped something," she squawked in a passable imitation of Donald Duck.

Dull blue eyes stared back at her from beneath a lowered brow and Vera came to the swift conclusion that, though the curtains might be open, there was no one at home.

"Wassup?" someone asked, though mystifyingly the man's mouth didn't move. The apparent ventriloquism was explained when a smaller man stepped out from behind the first.

"I said, you seem to have dropped something," she repeated, showing him the scrunched-up wrapper.

Regretting her decision to challenge them, her eye fell on the red writing

"Not mine, lady," he told her. "That yours, Don?"

The giant Don peered at the scrap as though he'd never seen its like before. "Nuffing to do with me, Rick."

She was fast beginning to regret her decision to challenge them over something so trivial when her gaze fell to the wrapper. As she glimpsed the ruby-red writing inside she gave a start, her fingers closing around it like a Venus fly-trap around its prey.

"So you're absolutely sure this doesn't belong to either of you?" she asked. The one named Don scowled and shook his head, while Rick just smirked.

"I guess it just fell out the sky!" he said, tossing a wedge of chocolate into his mouth. The other one sniggered and slapped him admiringly on the back, before they both turned and walked away.

Opening her hand, Vera smoothed the wrapper flat on the wall.

Congratulations, she read, *you have won a weekend in Paris in our Heavenly Holiday Instant Win Competition. To claim your prize...*

She threw back her head and laughed.

"Happy anniversary, Jack, darling. Looks like I'm off to Paris after all!"

"I've always loved entering competitions and have won many prizes over the years – including £10 from an instant win inside a carton of fruit juice tossed over my garden wall!"

Brain BOOSTERS

Missing Link

The answer to each clue is a word which has a link with each of the three words listed. This word may come at the end (eg HEAD linked with BEACH, BIG, HAMMER), at the beginning (eg BLACK linked with BEAUTY, BOARD and JACK) or a mixture of the two (eg STONE linked with HAIL, LIME and WALL).

ACROSS

2. Captain, Play, Splinter (5)
7. Book, Gap, Light (4)
8. Box, Operated, Pound (4)
9. Big, Hill, Notch (3)
10. Moor, Red, Shooting (6)
11. Brownie, Bullet, Strong (6)
13. Birthday, Flash, Playing (5)
14. Bean, Front, Road (6)
15. Mask, Natural, Stove (3)
16. Bath, Gum, Speech (6)
18. Patch, Roads, Victoria (5)
21. Bag, Cake, Finger (6)
23. Bird, Prince, Vice (6)
25. Along, Down, Shoulders (3)
26. Dance, Owl, Storming (4)
27. Book, Message, Sub (4)
28. By, Guide, Yellow (5)

DOWN

1. Admiral, Guard, Lights (4)
2. Control, Cover, Under (6)
3. Hebrides, Most, Space (5)
4. Chilli, Green, Jalapeno (7)
5. Packed, Replay, Stations (6)
6. Half, Pot, Size (4)
12. Bed, Cold, Eye (5)
13. Ice, Stock, Sugar (5)
15. Election, Major, Practice (7)
17. Boat, Skin, Split (6)
19. Animal, Civil, Human (6)
20. Jungle, Myth, Sprawl (5)
22. Avocado, Conference, Shaped (4)
24. Best, Door, To (4)

Solutions on page 161

Biscuits

Have you ever experienced that awful moment in a job interview when your thoughts crumble and turn to mush?

By Della Galton

o if you were a biscuit, what sort of biscuit would you be?"

For a moment Kerry was taken aback. Despite all her preparation, despite the fact that she wanted this job more than she'd ever wanted anything – or perhaps because of these things – she felt breathless.

The interviewer's face was deadly serious. He sat opposite her in his dark suit, a slight frown between his blue eyes.

"Er," she began as he leaned forward expectantly. To her dismay her mind had gone totally blank.

Bob Jackson, of Jackson and White Copywriters, watched her as she scanned the room for inspiration.

"I'd be a – a ginger nut," she said firmly. "That's what I'd be."

Bob smiled. That was a good start. "And why's that?"

"Because they're spicy, hard... um... working and reliable. You know what you're getting with a ginger nut. And they have a – er – history of longevity. By that, I mean," she waved a hand as if demonstrating an obvious point, "they've been around for ever. Everyone knows what a ginger nut is – not like some of these newfangled biscuits that no-one's ever heard of."

"Is that so?" His smile broadened. "A hard-working ginger nut, eh? As opposed to a newfangled biscuit. Could you name one of these newfangled biscuits for me, Kerry?"

"Well, no. I don't think I could. I mean

Kerry's gaze alighted on a magazine. Her brain made a tenuous connection

Kerry bit her lip. She really needed this job – even if they were all as nutty as fruitcakes. It was the work she loved best plus a great salary, which was handy as she and her sister planned to flat-share and were saving madly for the deposit.

Kerry's gaze alighted on a picture of a ginger cat on the cover of a magazine on the floor. Her brain made a tenuous connection.

that's the point I'm making, Bob." She said his name with a little flicker of satisfaction. Number one tip in the book of interviewee techniques – *remember your interviewer's name. Make it personal.* "They're not memorable, Bob, are they?" she went on. "Not in the slightest. No-one can remember their names. Not like ginger nuts."

Continued overleaf...

ILLUSTRATIONS: THINKSTOCK, MANDY DIXON

She said his name with a flicker of satisfaction

Continued from previous page

"No. You could be right." He'd stopped smiling now and was looking thoughtful. Oh dear, maybe she'd gone too far with this daft biscuit analogy. But after all, he had started it.

"So – to recap, you're hard-working and reliable, so far so good – but how about your weaknesses, Kerry? Do you have any of those?"

"Doesn't everyone?" She took a deep breath and met his gaze. "I struggled with dyslexia when I was at school, which was hard, but it won't affect my work in my job. I promise you that."

She hesitated. "I guess you could say I was a broken ginger nut," she ventured. "You know how you can buy those boxes of broken biscuits that are cheaper – because they're not whole, but they taste the same obviously…"

Oh gosh. He was frowning now. Perhaps she shouldn't have mentioned the dyslexia. But she wanted to be honest. She looked him square in the face.

"Broken biscuits are just as good as your average biscuit in the – er – big scheme of things," she said, aware that she was gabbling now. "Truly, they are, you should try some."

"Quite," he said. "Well – thank you very much, Ms Williams, I think that's probably enough for now. I'll be in touch. We have your contact details, don't we?"

He was standing up and he didn't look pleased. Or perhaps he was just anxious to get rid of her because he thought she was a complete nut.

And whose fault was that? She bit her lip as she went out of the door. A ginger nut, for goodness' sake. Why, oh why hadn't she stuck to being a nice ordinary shortbread? Or a chocolate digestive? Everyone liked chocolate digestives.

So, how did it go?" Meg asked when she called round later that day. "Any joy, do you think?"

"I'm not sure." Kerry frowned. "It was going great… but I may have blown it."

She told her sister what had happened.

"I shouldn't have mentioned broken biscuits – or said they'd be cheaper. He probably thought I meant I'd be cheap to employ. Not to mention defective! Oh gosh. He practically shoved me out the door after that. He was gorgeous too," she added sadly. "Not that that's a factor, of course."

"Oh, I don't know," Meg said with a wink. "It never hurts to have a gorgeous boss. Was he single?"

"I don't know," Kerry said miserably. "I don't suppose I'll ever find out now!"

"I'm sorry," Meg said and gave her a hug. "Don't worry. There'll be other jobs."

"He practically shoved me out of the door after that. He was gorgeous too"

Kerry was getting ready for work the next day when she got the text from Jackson and White.

Would the broken ginger nut be available to start on Monday 5th? If so, please contact our office to discuss contracts.

Hey – so it was the strangest job offer she'd ever had – but after a year of trying it was also the most satisfying.

"Bob Jackson asks everyone that question," said Sue, Bob's secretary, on

She heard Bob calling her

her first day. "He says it tells him a lot about someone's personality."

"Right," Kerry said, glancing towards the glass office of her new employer. "Actually, I thought I'd blown it. He seemed really keen to get rid of me after I mentioned broken biscuits."

"That's because you touched a nerve," Sue said, her eyes kind. "You mentioned dyslexia which is something he suffers from himself. In fact he's got a bit of a chip on his shoulder about it. I only know because I edit his monthly reports."

"Blimey," Kerry said, but she was interrupted by Bob's voice.

"Kerry, have you got a minute?"

"Of course," she said, putting down her coffee and hurrying into his office.

"I just wanted to go through a few things with you." He smiled at her. "Take a seat."

Twenty minutes later, as she got up to go, he said, "One more thing, Kerry. Thank you for being honest with me about the dyslexia."

She nodded, feeling her face heat up.

"I gather Sue told you it's something we have in common."

"Yes," she said, aware of his sudden seriousness and wondering if it was her place to tell him it was OK. That it wasn't such a massive handicap these days.

There was a pause.

"It made my schooldays hell," he went on softly. "It wasn't really recognised then. I was made to feel stupid. Like I was somehow defective, broken… So your broken biscuit analogy, while clever and quite amusing, took me back there."

"Crumbs," she said, and slapped a hand over her mouth. "Oh gosh, I didn't mean –"

To her relief he was smiling. "I think you and I are going to get along very well," he added and linked his hands together on the desk.

No ring, Kerry observed, feeling her heart do a little skip and a jump. Not, of course, that this meant he wasn't attached, but it was an excellent start.

"We clearly have a lot in common," Bob was saying. "The same sense of humour too, from what I can see. Just don't stop making me laugh. Don't hold back. Think you can manage that?"

She hesitated, but only for a second.

"Piece of cake, Bob," she answered with a wink.

THE AUTHOR SAYS… **"If you enjoyed this story about biscuits, I hope you might enjoy my novel too. *Ice and a Slice* is about drinking (oh, and also love, friendship and dysfunctional families)."**

Queen Of The Road

My wonderful dad gave me my first truck when I was four. Ever since then, I'd wanted to follow in his tyre tracks…

By Julia Douglas

he paint was like a mirror. It reflected my forearm, work shirt rolled to the elbow, as painstakingly I buffed the wing to perfection.

You could see your face in that, lass! Dad's words floated into my head as they always did, and I smiled. I could indeed see my face, framed by the fluffy white clouds of a bright autumnal morning. It was a strong face, more handsome than beautiful, with a lot of Dad in it – especially at the moment, with no make-up and my hair pulled back under a band.

It was seven am and I hadn't had a shower yet, much less breakfast. Plenty of time for that later.

In Dad's book, and mine, prepping the truck always came first. Besides, I liked these moments alone in the yard. It gave me space to think.

Dad bought me my first truck when I was four. It was a Scammell eight-wheeler with the name of a brewery on the side. I think he wanted a boy to follow in his footsteps, or his tyre tracks, really. It's probably why he called me Laurie. How that joke's worn thin over forty years!

As a kid I didn't mind. I must have put a hundred thousand miles on that foot-long truck, pushing it all over the carpet, pretending I was Dad, making his drops from one end of the country to the other.

When I was a bit older he'd take me out on the road with him. I was barely big enough to see out of the cab window. But how I loved the view, with the wind in my hair, as we flew along the motorway. Bridges, farms, towns and trains. They looked like a life-sized toy set as they sped by. Then there were all the other trucks we passed: Atkinson, Foden, Man, Leyland… I knew every make.

His mates made a fuss of me in the transport cafes – although I'd get the odd crack even then: "Just don't let her get behind the wheel, Tel. There's enough women drivers on the road!"

Well, I was determined there'd be another one.

None of my friends understood. "Why d'you want to drive a big smelly lorry?"

Even Mum wasn't keen. "Won't you be lonely driving up and down the country every day?" she fretted.

But as Dad used to tell her, with a wink in my direction, "Some of us have got diesel in our veins – 'aven't we, lass?" It

Continued overleaf…

PICTURES: KIRK HOUSTON, THINKSTOCK

Continued from previous page

made me feel dead proud to be like him.

I got some funny looks when I took my HGV driving test – but I had the cleanest lorry. Dad spent the whole weekend polishing it.

"Like they're going to pass me for having a clean truck," I joked, as he buffed his hard-working Iveco to show condition. But Dad believed in first impressions.

"You never get a second chance to make one," he reasoned. Then he gave me a tiny gold pendant, in the shape of a truck. "For luck." He smiled.

I passed first time, and wondered if that good luck charm twinkling at my throat had worked. Of course, I knew it was Dad I had to thank for spending so many hours teaching me to drive.

He got me a job with one of his mates and I was out on my own in a Volvo artic the very next day. Boy, did I think I was something! Until I got lost looking for my first drop. No SatNav in those days, and I ended up in a cul-de-sac on a Leeds housing estate.

So much for the good luck charm, I thought ruefully, as I gazed in my mirror at the narrow, twisting road behind me; the parked cars on either side.

A bunch of bin men had to help me back out. They were nice lads, but you should've heard the guffaws as they waved me on my way. "Women drivers, eh?"

I had a lot to learn in those first few years. Like how noisy the rain on a cab roof can be when you're trying to sleep in an Ayrshire lay-by. And how a woman in a truck-stop eats alone. Most of the lads are married, see. They work long hours away for a week at a time. They don't want to risk being seen getting friendly with a lady in case the gossip gets back home.

So I learned how to change my own wheels and replace my own light-bulbs by torchlight, with the puddles splashing up my back as the other drivers flew by. And I discovered that I had to work twice as hard to get half the respect.

When transport managers were divvying up the work, it was the men who got the best jobs and the overtime. I know they had families to support. But I was doing the same work – and often better than them.

"It's so *unfair,* Dad!" I whined, in tears, on a payphone from some truck stop in the middle of nowhere.

"Just keep smilin', lass," he told me. "And remember why you do the job."

"Diesel in my veins," I mumbled. And as I fingered the truck-shaped pendant at my throat I smiled in spite of myself.

Because, for all the hassles, I loved my work. From the moment I pulled out of the yard, I was my own boss – just me, the steering wheel and the open road. I could never have worked in an office with someone breathing down my neck all day. Could never have stayed in one place two days running, for that matter.

We live in a beautiful country, and the view through my windscreen was an ever-changing work of art – from sunrise over the Dales to rainbows over the Lakes and sunsets on the Clyde. I hauled abroad, too. Out through Europe to Poland; down to the south of France; up into the Netherlands.

I was seeing the world and it didn't cost me a penny. In fact, I was being paid. What more could a girl ask for?

Oh, and don't let me give you the impression all men have a problem with women drivers. It was how I met Dave, after all. He was the goods-in manager of a supermarket in Manchester. He always had a hot cuppa waiting while they unloaded me at 2am.

"Do you know what I like about you, Laurie?" he said one night, as I huddled beside the little gas heater in his office.

"My beautiful face and lovely figure?" I joked – I was in my bulky hi-vis coat.

Dave reddened.

"I was going to say it's because you always come in with a smile – not grumbling and complaining like all these other so and sos."

"It's the way my dad taught me to work." I grinned. "Keep a clean truck, get there on time and..."

I tailed off, because the way Dave was looking at me so shyly was sending a funny feeling right through me.

I watched them, chin stretched up to the window and the wind in their hair

"But since you mentioned your beautiful face..." He smiled nervously.

Dad drove me to the church in a Daf tractor unit with white ribbons on the front. It made a change climbing down from the cab in a veil and heels instead of work gloves and steel toecaps.

Dad rushed around to the passenger door in his tailcoat and top hat, ready to help me out with my train. He needn't have worried about the lace touching the cab steps. He'd shone every inch of that truck up like a royal carriage, and as he walked me up the aisle, I felt like a princess on his arm.

My "something old" was the truck necklace Dad gave me when I took my test. Not that I'd need a good-luck charm with Dave – we were made for each other.

A year later, I made my proudest delivery. She tipped the scales at 9lb 1oz, and arrived about as late as a baby can be.

"Who'd expect a woman driver to deliver on time?" I joked as I held my most precious cargo in my arms.

I think Dad would have liked a grandson and, if I'm honest, I wouldn't have minded a boy myself, to grow up sharing my love of trucks. But the next two were girls as well. Dad made sure they all got lorries on their birthdays and when they were older I'd take them out in my cab.

As I watched them, with their chin stretched up to the window ledge and the wind in their hair, I remembered all the trips I'd taken with Dad at their age – and how those journeys had shaped me.

I guess some women might have given up a job like mine when they had a family. But I had diesel in my veins. "The country has to eat, and we have to deliver the goods," as Dad used to say.

Dave did most of the parenting. He must have been one of the first stay-at-home dads. He did a grand job, and always had a hot cuppa waiting when I rolled in at silly-o'clock in the morning. It was just like the old days in his office. Except that instead of huddling around a gas heater, I had a pair of loving arms to slip into.

Continued overleaf...

Continued from previous page

The only time it hurt to be away so much was when one of the kids was ill, or if there was an emergency at home.

Like the night Mum phoned to say Dad had been rushed to hospital.

"It's his heart," she sobbed. "He was climbing down from the cab when he suddenly collapsed and couldn't breathe."

I was only fifty miles away. I'd been driving all day, I was exhausted and it was snowing hard. But I was a great driver – so I thought. Determined to get to the hospital, I put my foot down.

I could see the lights of the stricken car and I knew what Dad would have done

Amid the blizzard, red lights flared and slithered in front of me. A car had hit a snow bank and slewed across the road.

I hit my brakes and then I was skating sideways. Forty tons of trailer was about to jack-knife and crush the car in front.

Foot off the brake! Dad's voice yelled in my head. *Steer into the skid!*

It was as if his hands were on the wheel over mine. Somehow I pulled out of the skid and swerved past the car, missing it by an inch. I pulled over and sat shaking, holding the lucky pendant at my throat.

"Women drivers, eh?" I muttered.

I knew I should press on, that every lost minute might mean not seeing Dad again. But in my mirror I could see the lights of the stricken car and I knew what Dad would have done.

Hands trembling, I put my rig in gear and backed up to tow the car out of the road before someone hit it.

When I finally got to the hospital, Dad was feeling better. He tapped his chest and smiled weakly.

"Doc said I've had too many motorway fry-ups. But there's a few miles in me yet."

There were, too. But as I hugged him with relief, I knew the day he'd finally have to hang up his keys would be a sad one.

You could eat your breakfast off that, Dad!" I said, as I gave the cab step a final polish. I stepped back and admired the black vintage Ford seven-tonner I'd hired for his final journey.

Forty trucks came from all over the country to make up the procession, and as I drove slowly along the high street with Dad's casket and all the flowers in the open back of the Ford, people lined the pavement to watch us go by.

I think Dad would have been proud. I hope he's proud of me, too. I run my own haulage firm now, with all three of my girls out driving with me. It's called Women Drivers!, with an exclamation mark to get the crack in before anyone else.

But, funnily enough, we don't get too many jokes, because we're making quite a name for ourselves out there. We don't drive pink trucks or anything like that. We just get the goods where they're supposed to be, on time and with a smile… just the way Dad taught me.

THE AUTHOR SAYS...

"This story is dedicated to all the truckers who travel the country day and night, bringing us everything we eat and use."

Brain BOOSTERS

Word Wheel

You have ten minutes to find as many words as possible using the letters in the wheel. Each word must be three letters or more and contain the central letter. Use each letter once and no plurals, foreign words or proper nouns are allowed. There is at least one nine-letter word.

Average: 21 words
Good: 22-31 words
Excellent: 32-41 words

O E T D S E N C
G

Two Sudoku

Fill in each of the blank squares with the numbers 1 to 9, so that each row, each column and each 3x3 cell contains all the numbers from 1 to 9.

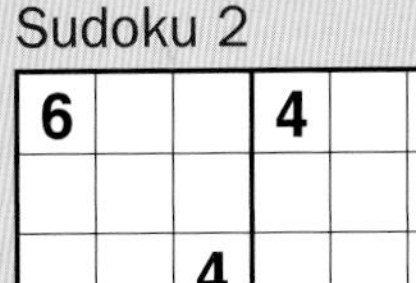

Sudoku 1

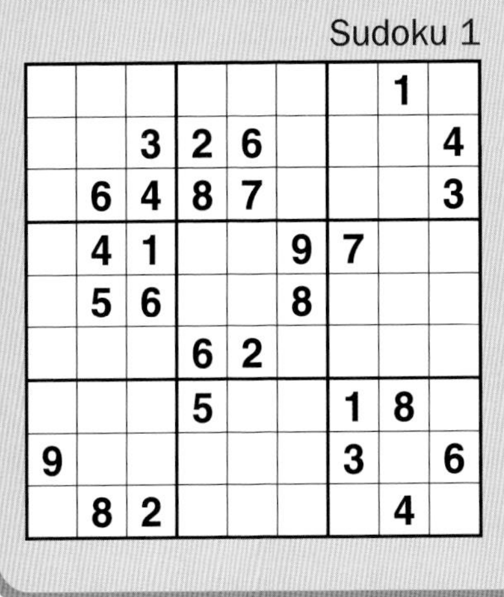

							1	
		3	2	6				4
	6	4	8	7				3
	4	1			9	7		
	5	6			8			
			6	2				
			5			1	8	
9						3		6
	8	2					4	

Sudoku 2

6			4			2	9	
							1	
		4			1			
1					4		7	5
				3		4		
		5	2				8	
5				7				3
4	8		3		6			
			9			8		2

Solutions on page 161

It's My Party

In spite of all their careful planning, Amber's twenty-first celebrations were turning out to be full of surprises...

By Claire Buckle

"How's it going, Dave?" Stef asked as she pushed open the kitchen door.

She'd left her husband kneeling amongst numerous poles, plastic pegs, and lengths of nylon rope laid out in neat rows on the wooden deck.

Two hours on, he was in the same place but the neat rows had blurred into a jumbled mess. Stef blew out a shaky breath. She'd hoped he'd have made a start by now – no, actually, she'd hoped it would be almost done.

Picking her way between the paraphernalia of the deconstructed marquee, she moved closer.

"Watch where you're treading," he said with a frown.

"I am, and there's no need to scowl," she muttered, struggling to keep her voice calm. The marquee needed to be assembled quickly; that's if the weather report was to be believed. "Looks like you could do with some help."

He waved a piece of paper at her. "Why don't they have written instructions in plain English instead of this rubbish?"

She took it from him, frowning at the numbered diagram. "It can't be that difficult, surely? Drawing's an international language."

"Not in my book," he grumbled.

She handed the instructions back and glanced at the darkening sky.

"I really want this party to be perfect, something extra special to look back on while she's away," she said in a small voice, rubbing the goose bumps from her arms.

"Don't go getting upset again," he said, standing up and stilling her hand as she began pulling at the yellow and gold beads of her bracelet. "We've been through all this. Thousands of girls go travelling – Amber's going to be twenty-one soon, a grown woman."

"But I wanted her to come home after uni. Find a job. She's all we've got – and I miss her."

She noticed Dave's jaw tighten and a muscle start working in his cheek.

"The job market will still be open in a year's time, Stef, and we have each other."

"I know – I'm sorry. It wasn't meant to to come out like that." She put her arms around him, the soft lambs' wool of his

"I wanted her to come home, find a job. She's all we've got and I miss her"

Continued overleaf...

PICTURES: MANDY DIXON, THINKSTOCK

Continued from previous page

jumper warming her chilled skin. "It's just… you know… if only…"

"No more 'if only's, Stef." Dave reached behind him and unhooked her hands. "Come on, get yourself a jacket and let's get this contraption up, otherwise there won't be any room for a party."

It was late afternoon before the two of them, having fathomed the correct position of umpteen different-sized poles and grappled with the unwieldy plastic covering billowing like a parachute in the gusting wind, finally managed to fix the marquee to the back of the house.

Dave looped fairy lights around the roof poles inside the tent and Stef flicked the switch. Seeing the result, they both smiled. Shaped like rosebuds, the pre-blossom cocoons bathed the walls in a delicate pink. Now all they could do was pray that the weather held.

The rain began a couple of hours later, squally showers worsening to torrents during the evening. The marquee flapped and fluttered its protest against the frantic lashing, keeping Stef and Dave awake most of the night.

When sleep eluded them they kept watch from their bedroom window, expecting at any moment to see it take off and land amongst the tangle of weeds and overgrown bushes masquerading as next door's garden.

Next morning they surveyed the damage. Deep channels of water had collected along the roof edge, causing precarious sagging. The poles had bent under the strain and the floor was wet where rain had seeped through.

"At least it's still intact," Dave said.

"Only just," she replied, miserably.

"Come on, I'll push the water off the roof, dry the floor out with those heaters we've got, fix up that shelf you want for the drinks and it'll be just fine. All we need is for Amber's friend to do his bit sorting out the music and we're laughing."

Stef took a couple of deep breaths. "Why? What else has happened?"

But laughing was the last thing on Stef's mind when she answered the phone later that day. It was Amber, calling from her university in Leeds.

"Matt's let me down with the music," she wailed. "He's landed a brilliant gig miles away, a top club he's been trying to get in with for months. He's really sorry, but says he can't miss this chance. It could be his big break. But that's not all."

Stef took a couple of deep breaths and concentrated on keeping her voice tranquil.

"Why? What else has happened?"

Amber's voice broke. "This has been such a rubbish week," she babbled. "Some of my friends can't come. They've either got assignments due in, or exams coming up. Everyone is stressing over work and deadlines and the weather's crap. Now, with Matt pulling out, I wish I hadn't bothered with a party. I feel like cancelling the whole thing."

"Oh, no, Amber!" Stef couldn't keep the panic from her voice. "We can't do that. A twenty-first is extra-special."

Visions of their Herculean efforts with the marquee, the food she'd bought and the cake she was having made flashed across Stef's mind. She wanted it to be an unforgettable party.

"We're having family too, they'll make the numbers up and you said you'd invited quite a few old college friends. And you're not telling me that *none* of your uni friends can come?"

"Only some of them can," Amber whimpered.

"Come on, sweetheart," Stef said, desperate to jolly both of them along, "we'll find another deck or disco, or whatever's needed."

"Oh, Mum, it's not that easy. I want house music, not party songs."

"All right, all right. What about the music on your iPod?"

There was a groan.

"I don't listen to dance music," was the agitated reply, "and I don't have time to download a massive playlist. I've still got an essay to finish before I come back."

"I'll have to have a ring round, see what I can do, although it's pretty short notice with the party only two days away." Stef felt close to tears.

"You don't have to remind me," Amber snapped, but instantly added, "Sorry, Mum, I'm just gutted."

"I'll sort it out, love. I don't want you getting upset. So much rests on the next couple of months with finals coming up."

"I'll be fine. Once the essay's done I'm all up to date," Amber said.

Stef wasn't convinced. Her daughter's voice sounded small, weak, like a vulnerable child's.

"Are you sure?"

"Don't fuss, Mum, I said I'm OK."

Within minutes of saying goodbye to her daughter, Stef was on the phone to her husband.

"Sorry to call you at work," was always her intro when there was a problem. She quickly summarized her phone call. "Is there anywhere we can get this equipment? Mind you, even if we can, how much will it cost? We're already over budget. And she wants music she likes. Oh, Dave, she said she wants to cancel..."

"OK, stop there," Dave said. "Let me have a think and I'll sort something out, even if it's not exactly what Amber wanted. This party's going ahead come hell or high water – and we've already had more than enough of the water."

"Let me have a think. This party's going ahead – come hell or high water"

"All sorted," was Dave's greeting on arriving home from work that night. Stef was half-heartedly preparing dinner, making a cheese sauce. Not that she had

Continued overleaf...

Continued from previous page

much appetite for it anyway.

"What do you mean?"she asked.

He shrugged off his jacket and hung it over a kitchen chair. "I sent an email to all my work colleagues. A bit of a begging message, explaining I needed someone, anyone, who could provide music for a twenty-first party, and Nick from sales saved the day."

"Really?" Stef rubbed her hand along the taut muscles at the back of her neck. "I hope it's the right sort of music."

Dave sighed and slumped into the chair. "Basically, we're in a bit of a predicament. We don't have much choice. Nick's willing to do the party as a favour. He's a bit of an extrovert – admits it's all a bit of fun for him… a hobby. Mainly just for family and friends. He's taken pity on us, so let's just hope for the best."

"I see. Well done. Things are looking up at last," she said bravely, even if she didn't quite believe it. The heaters had been on all day but the marquee floor was still damp. Two buckets were underneath leaks and several eyelets had ripped in the wind, leaving nylon cord dangling, sodden and dripping.

Turning back to the cooker, she saw she'd left the gas on low. The sauce had turned to lumps and stuck to the pan.

"Tell you what," she said with a tight smile, "I'm not hungry. How about you pop out and get yourself fish and chips?"

As Stef pulled on her new silver-grey jumper and stepped into her faithful black evening trousers, she heard Hannah and Grace chattering as they came upstairs. They were Amber's old school friends, arriving early to relive their teenage years, spending time getting ready together.

She was pleased the girls still had that special bond. If only they'd been able to take a year out, leave their jobs and go travelling with Amber – instead of the uni friends whom Stef hardly knew.

Her throat tightened as she remembered how inseparable the girls had been when they were younger. The three of them could have been sisters.

Sitting at her dressing table, Stef pulled opened its deep bottom drawer and took out a pink painted box with the words *Baby Memories* printed in white on the hinged lid. Opening it, she rummaged through the keepsakes from the past twenty years; a yellow dummy, the curl from Amber's first haircut, preserved in a tiny plastic bag, pink baby bootees, and a section cut from the Ninny, the name they gave Amber's white satin-trimmed comfort blanket. There was also a pile of photos, mostly of herself and Dave with Amber on every birthday since the first.

There she was, that tiny scrap, red and wrinkled, lying in the incubator

Underneath was the picture she was looking for. She rubbed her thumb over its shiny surface. Twenty-one years. How was it possible that amount of time had passed? There she was, that tiny scrap, red and wrinkled lying in the incubator, connected to wires and tubes, her head covered by the miniature white knitted hat that now lay in the corner of the box.

With a sad ghost of a smile, she replaced the picture, closed the box and

returned it to the drawer. She slid on her yellow and gold beaded bracelet, Dave's present to her twenty-one years ago, and headed downstairs.

Stef began carrying the foil trays laden with party food from fridge to table. She popped a ham and mustard triangle into her mouth and fussed with the cress dressing surrounding the neat rows of sandwiches. She was busy stacking paper plates and napkins when the girls made their entrance.

"Wow!" Stef exclaimed. "Don't you all look gorgeous."

Amber twirled on high wedged heels showing off her short lacy dress, the colour of the night sky, and flicked back her glossy sable hair. Stef fought the urge to comb her fingers through the silky waves, as she had when Amber was a child, knowing now the gesture would be shrugged off. A heady mix of pungent perfume drifted across the room, reminding Stef she'd forgotten to spray any on herself.

"I love my present, Mum." Amber brushed Stef's cheek with a swift kiss.

Continued overleaf...

Continued from previous page

She held her arm out, admiring a chunky designer watch, the black face on a gold linked strap surrounded by crystals.

"It's gorgeous," agreed Hannah. "I want one." She pouted and giggled. Linking arms, the three walked into the marquee and Stef watched as they began creating cocktails from the selection of bottles Dave was arranging on his "bar", a makeshift shelf of plywood.

"This is sweet," Stef heard Hannah say, "even with the leaky bits." She could hear them laughing. At least, they could see the funny side.

"When's the music coming, Dad?" Stef caught Amber's remark.

As though on cue, there was a knock. Stef hurried into the hall and answered the door to a balding middle-aged man in a paisley shirt. He placed a large aluminium case at his feet and stuck out his hand.

"Nick Chambers, disco king." He treated Stef to a wink and a wide grin.

Her daughter's crumpled expression told her Nick wasn't what she'd hoped

Battling to bring her raised eyebrows under control, she forced a bright smile.

"Please, come in, go right through the kitchen." She stepped aside and called out, "Dave..."

She was about to close the door when a couple of cars pulled up. Recognising college friends of Amber's she waved them inside, following them with a "Help yourselves to drinks and food."

As yet more people arrived and the house began to fill, Stef was relieved some of the invites had been declined. She put her head round the dining-room door and watched her daughter hugging and kissing relatives and friends, accepting cards, flowers, presents, and wine. A pink helium balloon with *Twenty-One, Amber* in glittery letters floated to the ceiling.

Leaving Amber to her role as birthday girl, a chocolate champagne bottle in one hand and a glass one in the other, she went into the marquee.

Nick had opened his case and was busying himself with the equipment inside. Dave had fixed a sturdy length of plywood, not dissimilar to the bar, at waist height. He'd excelled himself in DIY for this party and Stef hoped it would be an indication of things to come.

"There you are. Mum..."

Stef turned. Amber was behind her. "What, love?"

"Is that him?" Her daughter's crumpled expression told Stef that Nick was not what she had hoped for. She shrugged and made a "what can we do?" face, thankful for another knock at the door.

A young man stood on the doorstep

with small speakers under each arm. Visible above his low-slung jeans was a wide band advertising the designer of his underpants. Wisps of fine fair hair poked out of his woolly hat.

"Speakers," he said, stating the obvious.

"Ah." She frowned, puzzled.

"Sorry, I should say. I'm Gil, Nick's son. I've brought these." He lifted the speakers a fraction.

"Fantastic," breathed Stef. "Your dad's all set, I think."

"Cool." He stepped inside. "I'll fix these up and then get my music."

"Your music?"

"Yeah, it's in the van. Dad said it's your daughter's twenty-first." He gave a lopsided grin. "Didn't think she'd want the eighties and nineties selection which is Dad's specialty."

Relief lifted her features and she would have liked to gather the young man in her arms and hug him. Instead, she said, "Go through," excitedly calling, "Amber, Amber, come and meet Gil..." as she followed him down the hallway.

Throughout the evening, the selection of Gil's music vibrated through the marquee. His collection had been greeted with whoops and appreciative cries, although Stef noticed that Nick was keeping a close watch over his son and the undoubtedly expensive equipment.

Stef and Dave's friends found solace from the noise by retreating to the dining room and closing the door. The old phrase "the joint is jumping" popped into Stef's head and she smiled.

"Happy?" Dave said at that moment, returning her smile.

She nodded. "Happy and relieved. They're having a great time."

Dave checked his watch.

"What about the cake?"

"Let's do it now," she replied.

"You see to it and I'll sort out the champagne." Dave went into the kitchen and started to fill trays of plastic flutes. The cake was secreted in the utility room. Stef lifted the towel covering the box, opened the side flaps and placed the candles – the numbers two and one – on the three-tiered sponge, amid the white and purple polka dots and above the looped lettering of *Happy 21st Amber*. She struck a match and touched the delicate wick of the One, then the Two.

On Amber's twelfth birthday they'd got the news. No point in more treatment

Twelve. It was the day of Amber's twelfth birthday when she and Dave had been given the news, the phone call confirming there'd be no point in more tests, no point in more treatment. No chance of more children.

Come along now, she told herself as tears threatened, *this is the important bit.* She lifted the base and with steady hands carried the cake through the kitchen and into the marquee.

Dave nodded to Nick and an instrumental *Happy Birthday* began. Everyone joined in, not quite in time nor in tune, but with gusto and enthusiasm. As Amber blew out the candles, a cheer went up. Stef placed the cake in the middle of the dining table and picked up

Continued overleaf...

Continued from previous page

a drink from the tray.

Dave raised his glass, and his voice.

"A toast to our lovely girl. We couldn't be more proud. To Amber. Happy birthday, sweetheart."

As everyone echoed Dave's words, Amber, blushing, stepped forward, and held up her hand for quiet.

"I want to say a massive thank you to my mum and dad for organising all this – it's turned out to be the best party ever. All my true friends and family have been absolutely fantastic and I've been really spoilt with all the gorgeous pressies. And," she looked over at Nick and Gil, "some cool music."

A couple of friends shouted agreement and clapped.

Amber said, "Hold on, not finished." She took a sip of champagne, hiccupped and giggled nervously. "Sorry… bubbles up my nose." Stef watched closely as Amber took a deep breath.

"It's my twenty-first but also, as some of you know, had she lived, it would have been my twin sister's."

One or two soft murmurings punctuated the air.

As Amber continued Stef almost didn't recognise this confident young woman, speaking movingly about her twin.

Jade, so tiny. Nowhere near as strong as Amber. Jade, whose life existed inside the incubator for those few heart-rending days. *If only,* Stef had thought so many times. *If only Jade had lived, if only they could have had more children.* But they were so very lucky to have Amber.

Precious, beautiful, poised Amber. In an instant Stef felt lighter as she listened to her daughter and realisation dawned.

It was time to let Amber, the fledgling adult, fly free.

"Wonderful… never expected that." Dave was congratulating and hugging his daughter as Stef, eyes glazed with tears, clapped along with everyone else.

"Did I do okay?" Amber's words were whispered.

If only, she'd thought so many times. Yet they were so lucky to have Amber

Stunned, Stef could only nod and squeak out, "Absolutely." Unexpectedly a song sprang to mind and she murmured the title in Nick's ear.

"Okay, everyone," Nick's voice rose above the noise. "Time for some more music. This is a special request from Stef, dedicated to Amber."

A cheer went up as Tina Turner began to belt out her famous song. Friends and family joined in with the chorus. Laughter and tears mingled as Stef joined in.

This time she felt only joy as she touched the cool beads on her bracelet – bright yellow Jade, a reminder of their glimpse of sunshine… and the endless glow of Amber, forever lighting their lives.

THE AUTHOR SAYS...

"A real-life struggle to construct a marquee in stormy weather inspired this story. However, unlike Stef's, my husband excels in DIY, and we have not one but four lovely grown-up daughters!"

Brain BOOSTERS

Missing Link

The answer to each clue is a word which has a link with each of the three words listed. This word may come at the end (eg HEAD linked with BEACH, BIG, HAMMER), at the beginning (eg BLACK linked with BEAUTY, BOARD and JACK) or a mixture of the two (eg STONE linked with HAIL, LIME and WALL).

ACROSS

1 Fly, Life, Master (4)
3 Process, Provoking, Reader (7)
9 Forward, Glass, Good (7)
10 Arm, Deck, Lift (5)
11 Deed, Role, Sub (5)
13 Foil, Meter, Static (5)
14 Brain, Cell, Ginger (4)
16 Finger, Hang, Toe (5)
18 Blooded, Front, Hearted (4)
19 Coat, Pig, Shirt (5)
21 Chip, Faced, Player (5)
23 Rider, Train, Writer (5)
24 Bank, Production, Stage (7)
25 Shop, Slip, Spread (7)
26 Agent, Paper, Reader (4)

DOWN

1 French, Furniture, Shoe (6)
2 Cold, Frozen, Hard (8)
4 Hedge, Road, Wash (3)
5 Dutch, Great, Sam (5)
6 Compost, Rubbish, Scrap (4)
7 Engine, Ring, Rod (6)
8 Pipe, Team, Ticket (5)
12 Ear, Set, Skinned (5)
15 Bermuda, Equilateral, Eternal (8)
17 Along, Quartet, Vest (6)
18 Anchor, Bridge, Up (5)
20 Hail, Out, Tropical (6)
21 Bourgeois, Four, Point (5)
22 Loop, Plug, Port (4)
24 Chess, Folk, Gentle (3)

Solutions on page 161

Rachel's Return

After a shattering loss comes the chance of a new start – but such deep emotions are not so easily resolved

By Kate Hogan

onscious of the sudden quickening of her heartbeat, Rachel turned off the main route and onto the narrow road which would take her downward towards the village and the harbour beyond.

She wondered for what seemed like the thousandth time if it would be wiser to put the car in reverse, get herself back on the main road and head straight for the motorway. She really hadn't planned this. Yet somehow she found herself, foot down, driving straight back.

To this place where she'd made her promise to Kevin. The promise she'd almost broken with Joe.

She hoped Kevin would know that everything had spiralled out of control. The unexpected panic, the sense of falling and losing her balance. She'd been off-kilter – wrong-footed – when Joe had kissed her.

She'd fled. Rushing back to the B&B she'd booked into for her first holiday in over four years, she'd paid the bill, throwing her things in the car and taking off without looking back.

Now here she was driving back into the past, pulling into a viewpoint lay-by, climbing from the car as if in slow motion. The breath caught in her throat.

The view was unchanged. The sweep of rock and headland, the curve of the bay, the rolling clouds – the threat of storm, the glimpse of harbour wall beyond the whitewashed cottages as beautiful now as it was then.

She fought the rush of tears that welled up behind her eyes and wondered whether it would have been like this for Kevin, her husband; Kevin with the laughing brown eyes and tireless smile.

She slammed the car door shut, aware now of the anger welling up inside her.

"When we come back," he'd said. His voice echoed down her memory.

But they'd never come back. Fate had intervened by stroking ice on a patch of road before a hairpin bend, by sending a

Continued overleaf...

Everything had spiralled out of control – she'd been off-kilter when he kissed her

Continued from previous page

child scurrying across the road after a wayward dog, and he'd gone. Kevin had gone – taken by the decree of fate.

Tears had refused to fall; instead, a cold armour of shock, tight as steel, had wrapped itself around her. Sometimes the tightness hurt, as if her very breath was being squeezed from her. But she held on.

The façade of normality was easier once she'd moved to London. The new people she met didn't know about the past, didn't know that she'd ever been any different from the quiet, introspective workaholic that she'd become.

This holiday, this chance to walk in the hills, had been her first tentative step back, but never – never – was it to find herself unexpectedly in the arms of another man. She felt the rush of shame, the sudden burning flush of heat on her wind-chilled skin. The gaping gulf of guilt was a freshly-formed new wound upon her heart. How could she? A man she'd known for less than a week.

She slung her bag over her shoulder, checked that she'd locked the car, pushed her hair back from her face and blinked back the tears still threatening to fall. She hadn't wanted to be involved with anyone else, ever. She'd made her promises to Kevin. She couldn't break them.

She started to walk, making her way to the harbour, the place where she'd promised Kevin she'd love him forever.

By the time she reached the first bend in the steep road her legs were beginning to feel weak, her heart pounding more violently with each step. Every turn, every emerging view, every scent and sound was conjuring images and memories of the past.

Would he forgive her? Would Kevin know that Joe meant nothing?

She'd made a mistake. She'd only teamed up with Joe because he'd lost his map, offering to share hers to save him returning in the fading light of evening to where he remembered placing it on a boulder while he admired the view.

"Excuse me," he'd said.

She'd turned in the direction of the voice and for a split second froze.

"I'm sorry, did I startle you?"

He'd stepped back, his face creasing into a nervous smile.

She'd taken in the backpack and walking boots, which introduced him as a fellow walker, and chided herself mentally for allowing wavy dark hair and a broad frame to play tricks on her mind.

Realising she was staring, failing to answer his question, she took a breath

He didn't look anything like Kevin. The features were sharper, his body more solid than athletic. Suddenly realising she was staring, failing to answer his question, she took a deep breath.

"Just a little, I hadn't expected to see anyone up here." She waved her arm to take in the expanse of countryside she'd been exploring.

He laughed and Rachel noticed that his eyes were blue, almost green. Not brown; not dark and deep like Kevin's.

"You looked miles away. I

didn't want to intrude but I seem to have lost my map. I could head back up to where I think I may have left it but…"

"The fading light," she'd said before he could finish. "It can become very dark quite suddenly."

"Yes," he'd said. "Once the sun – the light disappears it's even harder to discern the way safely."

Rachel had experienced an ache in her chest when he said it, had become silent remembering how the light in her life had gone so unexpectedly.

The seconds ticked by. Suddenly aware of how rude she must appear, standing and staring, she'd slowly refocused and asked which way he wanted to go, carefully unfolding her map as she did so.

She found the campsite he was heading to and pointed. "It's less than two miles. If you follow this track –" She'd pointed to a tiny dotted line as she spoke. "Then you just cross the bridge and go left following the river."

She waited, hoping he would turn and go. He didn't.

"Are you walking that way yourself?" he asked, his smile broad and open.

Rachel felt suddenly trapped. She wanted to be alone with her thoughts.

"I'm sorry," he said. "I'm invading your solitude."

She felt ashamed, aware that her expression alone must have answered his question. Forcing a smile, she shrugged.

Continued overleaf…

Continued from previous page

"Yes," she said. "I'm heading back down towards the village. I take a right at the bridge."

"Great," he said, slipping into step beside her as she turned to make her way across the heather-clad hill toward the path she'd identified.

By the time they'd reached the first bend in the steep road he had told what seemed to Rachel almost his entire life story. She supposed her own quietude had that effect on others at times – they rushed to fill in the silences.

His name was Joe. He was a software engineer and had four brothers.

"Whenever I get the chance I take a holiday like this – no computers, no staring at screens. I like the space and the quiet." He'd raised his arm to indicate the flight of a sparrowhawk and laughed. "It's like owning a piece of the world up here," he'd said, then turned towards her.

"Are you on holiday here yourself – or do you live here?" He paused, his gaze on her suddenly more intense. "I'm sorry; my mouth runs off on its own sometimes. I don't mean to keep asking questions, I don't know what's got into me. I haven't even asked you your name."

"Rachel," she'd said. "Rachel Barteth."

It had been so innocent. A fellow walker, someone to swap ideas with, an opportunity for identifying routes together; it had seemed no more than that when they'd agreed at the bridge to meet the following day to tackle one of the higher slopes.

By the end of the week she'd found herself waking in the morning with a sense of purpose. Each new trek had been a challenge. She'd ventured further into the hills and mountains than she'd ever have dared alone, had enjoyed Joe's chatter and his ability to identify so much of their surroundings – the birds, the wildflowers, even the names of clouds that sometimes scurried across the dome of sky that opened up above them.

She'd relaxed in spite of herself, surprised to hear the sound of her own laughter again. Safe in the knowledge that Joe's company was the company of a friend.

Then he'd caught her unawares.

The crumbling path, almost nothing, yet it had been enough to make her lose her footing and stumble on the path she'd planned.

He was kneeling beside her in a second; his arm curved around her shoulder in support, a look of earnest concern on his face.

"Joe, I… I'm OK." She'd tried to raise herself, extricate her body from his arms. He hadn't let her.

"Shshh." His voice was soft and low. "You hit the ground quite hard there." He'd stroked the hair back from her forehead. "You've quite a bump. I should

have held your hand – it's far too precarious near the edge."

It was. She should have pulled away. But she'd let him hold her – almost burrowed into his arms. Dizzy with the need for closeness. The warmth and scent of him a reminder of all that she'd lost.

"I could stay here forever," he'd said, his breath a caress upon her skin as his arms enfolded her more tightly.

His lips had found hers as he spoke. She'd suddenly pulled away, terrified of what she'd done, of what it meant.

"I need to get back," she'd said.

The memory caused her to tighten her hands into two small fists. She'd let him hold her. Let him kiss her. A man, another man: Joe, not Kevin.

She saw him before he saw her. He was moving on, too, walking the road with his backpack fully loaded. His tent and sleeping bag were rolled and secured. Head down, he was a danger to himself and passing cars on a narrow road.

She could have driven past, but she heard the roll of thunder. She sensed the heavens open, and slowed the car.

"Joe," she called.

He listened quietly as she told him about Kevin, about the years of burying herself in work, the continual frantic activity so she wouldn't have to think.

"Sometimes I felt so brittle, so empty, I thought I might crack into tiny pieces."

Her words hung in the silence, the rain that had made going any further in the car impossible now a blur around them.

"I think you've been brave, struggling to cope with the pain for so long"

Instinctively she raised her hand to blot out the thoughts, moved it swiftly across her face, tasted the saltiness of tears.

"I really am sorry, Rachel," he'd said when, despite his protests, she'd insisted she was perfectly fine to make her way back once they'd reached the bridge. "I thought… well, never mind."

He turned, and she'd watched him go.

Now she'd left him behind. She kept her eyes fixed on the ground beneath her, realising she couldn't face the harbour and the memories. Not today, maybe not ever. She wasn't ready.

She turned; she'd go back to the car, book herself into somewhere for the night and make her way back home in the morning.

There was a tremor in Joe's voice when he finally spoke.

"Rachel," he said. "I'm so very, very sorry that you've lost someone you loved, someone who gave your life so much meaning. I can't begin to understand how you feel, but my heart hurts for you. I think you've been very brave struggling to cope with the pain for so long."

He tentatively took her hand in his own and gently, very gently, began to stroke her fingers. She let him.

"But sometimes –" He paused. "We have to take a chance on moving on. I…" He slowed the stroking of her fingers and simply held her hand. "When I lost that map in the hills I had to take a chance on

Continued overleaf…

Continued from previous page

finding the right road, the right turning to somewhere where I'd be safe until I could adjust my compass and move on again." He turned towards her. "I never expected to find you there."

Rachel was aware of the softness of his touch and saw the tenderness in his eyes. She took a deep, shuddering breath.

"I guess – I guess you're right, Joe." She wiped away a stray tear. "I lost my map a long time ago."

The air was fresh with the scent of rain. The sun was carefree as it cast off the clouds and rose above the distant mountains beyond the harbour as she stood swathed in silence, gazing out along the golden curve of the bay to the rocky headland, which jutted out from the lush green of the land into the dark blue of the now tranquil sea.

She could see the fishing boats returning to the far harbour, thought how generations of fishing folk had coped with the loss of loved ones on stormy seas. The heartache, the pain, the loss, never forgotten, yet still the boats went out because life must go on – had to go on.

She could never break her promise to Kevin; she would, she knew, love him always. Nothing she could ever do would change that.

She let Joe escort her to her car. He waited while she started the engine and lowered the window, leaning down towards her as she turned her face to his, touching her cheek gently as he spoke.

"Promise me you'll call, Rachel," he whispered. "Even if it's just to let me know you're home safely."

She placed her hand over his. "I will, Joe," she said. "I'll call – I promise."

She meant it.

His blue, almost green eyes sparkled. She held his hand for no more than a moment before taking hold of the steering wheel.

"Promise me you'll call. Even if it's just to let me know you're home safely"

She sat back, slowly releasing the handbrake, the wind catching her hair through the open window as she turned to blow him a single kiss before accelerating towards the open road and the future ahead.

THE AUTHOR SAYS...

"I'm fascinated by the symbolic meaning of maps and compasses in relation to our inner journeys in life. Rachel's journey came as an expression of that fascination."

Teatime Treat

Tutti Fruttis

Ingredients

- 75g unsalted butter
- 75g golden syrup
- 30g plain flour
- 75g flaked almonds
- 25g unsalted pistachios, lightly crushed
- 50g chopped dried apricots
- 25g dried cranberries
- 25g glacé cherries, chopped
- 50g each of strawberry and orange flavour chocolate buttons, for baking
- 65g white chocolate, broken into small pieces

1 Preheat the oven to 180°C, Fan Oven 160°C, Gas Mark 4. Line 3 large baking trays with baking parchment. Melt the butter and syrup in a small saucepan. Remove from the heat and stir in the flour, nuts and fruit. Mix well.

2 Drop teaspoonful heaps, spaced well apart, on the prepared trays. Flatten to rounds approx 4cm in diameter and bake for 8-10min until lightly golden. Leave to firm up on the trays for 3min then transfer to a wire rack to cool completely.

3 Put each chocolate in a separate small heatproof bowl and set above saucepans of barely simmering water to melt. Spread the chocolate thickly over the underside of each biscuit, and place, chocolate side up, on a wire rack in a cool place to set before serving.

RECIPE: KATHRYN HAWKINS PHOTOGRAPHY: UPFRONT

Bad Hair Day

She's no hairstylist – but our granddaughter brightened our lives when it seemed that nothing ever could again

By Elaine Peake

uch! Careful, love, you're meant to leave the hair behind."

I can't help smiling as I watch my granddaughter's reflection in the dressing table mirror – her tongue protruding slightly from the corner of her mouth as she struggles to free my hair from the spiky blue plastic rollers.

"Nan, don't be a wimp. You used to pull mine much harder when I was little."

Lois's face is shiny, scrubbed clean and utterly beautiful. Hazy morning sunshine pours in through the window glinting off the tiny gold locket at her throat. I see her sometimes, deep in thought, holding it between her lips, running her tongue over the smooth gold surface… just as her mother had done.

The day of her birth had started in excitement and anticipation as we paced the hospital corridor waiting for news. When he finally came out of the white double doors, Tim, our good-natured son-in-law, was sobbing uncontrollably.

Women don't die in childbirth these days. The simple logic of these words screamed through my brain like a derailed locomotive, refusing to allow the truth, that our daughter was dead, to sink in.

Later we had stood at the graveside shielding our eyes from a low, brilliant sun. Lois had cried loudly and lustily.

Later that day when we were alone, Tim handed his new daughter to me.

"Will you help me, Eve?"

I looked down into the ruddy miniature face, feeling overwhelmed with the enormity of his request. Were we too old? What if we got it wrong?

I looked towards my husband, Mark, not for permission but for the silent reassurance that only he could give.

"Of course we will," I said.

Between the three of us, we did a good job. The proof stands behind me now, ruining a perfectly good hairdo. Tomorrow she will leave here, but there will be visits. The house will seem empty without her; Mark and I will have to learn to be a couple again and her father will have no excuse not to try to find love. She should have gone to France six weeks ago to take up a new teaching post, but she insisted on being here for me today.

I looked into the tiny face, overwhelmed with the enormity of Tim's request

"There you go, Nan, good as new," she says. "I'll just put your make-up on, then I'll leave you to get dressed."

Continued overleaf...

PICTURES: JIM DEWAR, THINKSTOCK

The locket had been her mother's

Continued from previous page

My outfit hangs in front of the mirrored wardrobe door. The white silk blouse contrasts sharply with the charcoal-grey pencil skirt. I frown as I notice a tiny black speck on the left shoulder.

"It's fine, Nan, you'll never see it once you're fully dressed. Now relax and let me make you beautiful."

"I thought you went to St Dominic's, not Hogwarts," I say, delighted when I get a laugh.

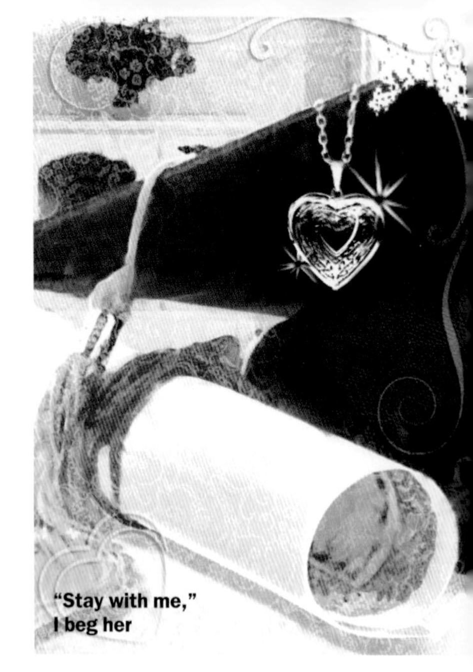

"Stay with me," I beg her

The cloudburst that threatened to submerge the marquee and render the grassy pathways unusable, stops as suddenly as it began. Lois escorts her father and grandfather to their seats before joining me in the long queue.

"This is your day, Nan – so savour it. Now go and knock 'em dead..."

"Won't be long now," she says cheerfully, in a vain attempt to quell my fluttering nerves.

"Will you stay with me?" I say as she helps me to adjust my clothing, putting the finishing touches to my appearance. She smiles tenderly as she tweaks my wayward tresses.

"This is your day, Nan – savour it." I feel the brush of her lips across my cheek. "Now go and knock 'em dead." She leaves me then, to return to her seat. I make my way along the red carpet and wait for my name to be called.

Lois was right about the mark on my blouse, the gown covers it completely – and, thankfully, the mortar board hides most of my hair.

It's because of her that I'm here today, picking up a first class honours degree. She brought me hope, comfort and the desire to live and learn again.

"Eve Parsons." The microphone squeaks slightly as the tall, bearded principal shouts out my name to a background of rousing applause.

I climb the steps up to the podium to receive my scroll. Then as the quietude resumes, there is an unmistakable and very unladylike wolf whistle.

The hair must look not bad, after all...

THE AUTHOR SAYS... "The loss of loved ones is inevitable. As we get older it's easy to forget that there are no endings – only new beginnings. My grandchildren are mine."

Fancy That!

Fascinating **Autumn flower** facts!

◆ Gladiolus takes its name from *gladius*, the Latin name for sword.

◆ **It's considered unlucky to give an actress flowers before a show – wait until after the performance.**

◆ The sunflower is the state flower of Kansas.

◆ **A rowan tree planted near your gate is said to keep witches out of your garden.**

◆ Broccoli is a flower as well as a vegetable.

The Iris takes its name from the Greek word for rainbow

The thistle became Scotland's national flower because its spikes hindered Viking invaders

◆ **Lifejackets were originally stuffed with dried sunflower stems.**

◆ A corsage is a small bouquet worn on a woman's dress.

The elder tree is known as the witch tree because no plants grow beneath it

◆ **On the ninth day of the ninth moon, the Chinese drink chrysanthemum wine to ensure a long life.**

◆ The blackberry lily of China is also known as the leopard flower.

◆ **The formal name for carnation, *dianthus* comes from the Greek for "heavenly flower."**

Ikebana is a Japanese style of floral design

Finding Uncle Alfred

It was going to be a long week, Jim thought, as he spotted his American cousin across the busy concourse…

By Hazel Moore

Not sure this was such a great idea," Jim Reynolds whispered to his wife as they stood in the middle of Heathrow's arrivals lounge.

"Neither am I," his wife whispered back, "but it's too late now."

They stood and watched their guests, Mr and Mrs Walt Purnell of North Platte, Nebraska, fuss and argue their way back across the concourse.

"You'd think she could get sunglasses before she left the States," Jim said.

"Walt," explained Di Reynolds, "tells me that Ginevra has to shop wherever she goes. He says," she coughed discreetly, "that she's like a cat spraying her territory."

Jim turned to stare at his wife, but the Purnells were now only a few feet away, unmistakable in their bright green outfits, and he turned to them and smiled.

"Well, Jimmy," Walt Purnell said cheerfully, "another hundr'an fifty dollars I might as well have put in the trash!"

"They are darling shades," Ginevra exclaimed. "Hey, Diane, I don't know if it's sunny in France, but I'm so looking forward to our trip!"

The Purnells were staying with the Reynolds until both couples set off on their tour of World War One battlefields. Walt and his wife had made contact while both families were researching family history.

It turned out that Jim Reynolds and Ginevra Purnell shared a grandfather, but that their branches of the family had long ago lost touch.

Their grandfather, Peter Reynolds, was born in 1893. One of Pete's sons, Ginevra's father, emigrated to The States. The other, Jim Reynolds' father, stayed in the UK.

"It's a crime that us cousins have never met, but the time has surely come!"

"It's a crime," Ginevra had yelled down the phone during their first long-distance call, "that us cousins have never met. But now we're both huntin' down Great Uncle Alfred, the time has surely come!"

Both Ginevra and Jim had separately been trying to trace details of Alfred

Continued overleaf…

ILLUSTRATIONS: THINKSTOCK, JAMES DEWAR

Continued from previous page

Reynolds, killed at the battle of Passchendaele in 1917, aged only twenty-two. He was their grandfather's brother. It seemed natural to Jim to invite his cousin to the UK, and accompany the Purnells to Belgium.

But, now that their guests were actually standing in front of them, brash, loud, grinning, perma-tanned and laden with luggage, Di and Jim were having second thoughts.

Walt told his wife to "hush up" and suggested he take all of them to the pub instead.

"I have never been in an English pub," he beamed. "I'm gonna get some rounds of bitter beer in!"

"The Fox and Firkin is a nice pub," Jim said, "and it's only five minutes away."

"So let's git goin'," Walt said with a grin. "Your car's in the garage, right?"

"I mean five minutes' walk," Jim said.

"Walk? Is the parking bad over there?" Walt asked, frowning with sympathy

Ginevra and Walt would be staying with Jim and Di in Surrey for two nights before they all got the coach to France and then on to Belgium. Before the first afternoon had ended, Di was feeling a deep sense of dread at the coming days.

Ginevra arrived at the house complaining of a runny nose.

"I'll just get along to the doctor for antibiotics," she said cheerfully.

Di explained that doctors don't usually provide diagnosis at six on a Sunday, especially with no appointment, and if they did, they would be unlikely to prescribe antibiotics for a head cold.

"But I always take antibiotics," Ginevra explained.

"If, on the other hand," Di said, "it was an emergency –"

"It is an emergency!" Ginevra declared.

The Purnells stared at him. "Walk?" they said in unison, turning to each other in astonishment.

"Is the parking bad over there?" Walt asked, frowning with sympathy.

"No," said Jim, "it's just a nice walk."

At the pub, Walt insisted on dusting off the old shove ha'penny board that had hung from the rafters for decades, and trying to get the astonished elderly gents at the bar to show him how to play.

Ginevra ordered a cocktail and Tina, the less-than-brainy barmaid, just stared at her, then finally pulled a bottle of tomato juice from the fridge and held it up hopefully.

Back home, several hours were spent sorting out the direction of the beds and the bedroom ventilation. Walt wasn't happy to face away from the door, and

Ginevra was accustomed to air conditioning, and didn't know how to sleep without it. They were endlessly apologetic and very merry, but it was eleven by the time that was sorted.

Then Walt asked about alarms.

"We've got a super system back home," he said proudly. "Ginny gets real anxious. Whole house is wired up at night."

Jim looked out of the window at their sleepy English village. A group of children wandered past on their way home from the swings in the dusk, barefoot.

"I'm sure you've no cause to worry," he said, trying to put them at ease.

But Ginevra got more and more jumpy, until Di suggested they used the loft room, once slept in by their sons.

"It would take the, er, the intruders," she suggested carefully, "a lot of effort to get past the dog, two floors of the house and a noisy loft ladder."

"And our bedroom," Jim added, "is on their path of, um, attack."

Ginevra seemed reasonably happy with this, and apologised again for fussing.

"It's quite alright," Jim said. "Now, let's get some sleep."

"If you guys don't mind," Walt said, "I'm gonna try out your British TV channels for a while. Can you get *Downton* on cable any time over here?"

The two days passed without too many further hitches. Walt talked a great deal about genealogy chat rooms, blogs and a network of amateur genealogists he seemed to spend twenty-two hours a day online with.

Ginevra was a walking encyclopaedia of British history, some of it rather inaccurate, and wanted constant detail on the Royals. She seemed to assume that Di was personally acquainted with the Duchess of Cambridge.

"Kate and Will live pretty near here, right?" she asked.

"Well, not really –"

"Might we bump into them, do you think?" Ginevra asked hopefully.

It rained for most of the journey to the Channel, across the choppy waters and into France.

Di lost an earring in a Kent service station, whereupon Ginevra insisted on buying her a new pair – enormous, horrible diamante items.

Walt had trouble finding meals that didn't contain things he wasn't allergic to, and Ginevra ordered all sorts of things "to go" that were not "to go".

Their ferry was delayed, and the coach driver was grumpy, but Walt ran a karaoke session of favourite songs of the trenches, accompanied by music from his laptop. By the time they reached the hotel just outside Ypres, Di was longing for a stiff glass of whatever wine the region offered.

"They're very... enthusiastic," she said to Jim when they collapsed side-by-side on their hotel bed.

"And they're kind," Jim added. He

Continued overleaf...

Continued from previous page
hesitated. "They're my relatives, Di. Is it very bad of me to say I can't really stand them?"

Di laughed and patted his arm. "Only three days left," she replied.

Walt and Ginevra exhausted the guide in the Passchendaele Memorial Museum by asking a hundred bizarre questions.

Ginevra asked for a doggy bag in a tiny restaurant, and almost made the shy waitress cry when she couldn't understand the term, then hugged the waitress until the girl was so horrified that she vanished into the back and didn't come out again.

Ginevra also shopped at every possible opportunity, until they could find nowhere to store all her bags.

On the final day, following days of battlefield visits, a beach and several museums, Di and Jim were nearly collapsing with bewilderment and fatigue at their extraordinary American cousins.

They were driven in the morning to the Tyne Cot War Graves Cemetery. It was a hot day when they climbed out of the coach, and Ginevra was yelling that she could not find her electric hand fan. Walt was saying that he should have brought shorter shorts, and Di was wondering how shorts could be shorter than Walt's. Jim was talking about a cup of tea, and saying that he hadn't had one since leaving Britain.

"Which seems like months ago," he hissed to Di.

Then they saw it – the stately archway to the cemetery, and, through it, a tall, slender column of white with a cross atop it, beautiful in the clear light, drawing them inside.

They all fell silent, and walked through.

Everywhere seemed to be shining white in the sunshine. Lines of graves, neat, silent, fringed with grass, stretched all around them.

Jim walked slowly, the others followed. A great sweeping colonnade with dozens of smooth white pillars curved around the regiments of graves. It seemed to circle and shelter them. Here and there a flash of red poppies drew the eye to a particular stone. The dark green tops of cypresses slowly moved in the breeze.

It was early, and the site was very quiet. Di heard a cockerel crow in distant farmland, and a pair of swifts flitted by over their heads.

Jim had a map that would enable them to find the marker for Corporal Alfred Raymond Reynolds. He held the map, and led the way.

When he stopped before a grave, near the centre of the cemetery, the others formed a small semicircle with him. All the business and noise of the preceding days seemed to recede.

"This is it," Jim said. He cleared his throat of the emotion rising in it. "This is Alfred, here."

"So young," Walt said, in a voice that Jim

and Di had never heard before, a soft, low voice. Walt lifted his bowed head to take in the lines of white graves. "So many."

Di saw Jim reach carefully into the front pocket of his rucksack for his battered photo of Alfred, and realised that Ginevra was doing something similar.

She and Jim were side-by-side, and their hands moved to compare the photos.

"The same picture," Ginevra said quietly.

"I didn't know you had one," Jim said.

Ginevra nodded. "It makes me sad," she said, "so I don't look at it much. I was kinda dreading getting it out once we got to this place."

She let out a single, quiet sob, and Di put an arm around her.

Di looked sideways at her husband and at Ginevra Purnell, and saw for the first time a family resemblance. Now that Ginevra looked serious, and gentle, she could see the strong jawline they shared with Alfred, and the large dark eyes.

Jim and Ginevra, as though sensing the same thing, turned to each other.

"Terrible for the family, back then," Jim remarked sadly.

"I wish wars would stop happening," Ginevra said simply. "I surely wish that. Poor Alfred. Just a baby. When I think of those trenches..."

Suddenly Walt rummaged in the huge bum bag that had been driving Di crazy on the coach. He drew out a crumpled piece of paper.

"Listen, I found this online," he said. "I don't want to be corny, but –"

Di and Jim both laughed softly, and Walt looked puzzled for a moment, but then turned back to his bit of paper.

"King George the Fifth," he said, "spoke this when he came here, you know. That guy Kipling wrote it for him – the *Jungle Book* guy." Walt coughed in preparation. "*I have many times,*" he read, "*asked myself whether there can be more potent advocate of peace upon Earth through the years to come, than this massed multitude of silent witnesses to the desolation of war.*"

They walked back to their coach some time later.

Di and Jim sat at the back while their cousins sat beside the driver, "Ready to annoy the life out of him again," said Di.

Jim looked at the backs of their heads. "Oh, but they're family, whatever they're like," he said.

"Yes, they are family," Di agreed. "And we all suffer loss in the same way, and feel the same regret."

Jim wrapped an arm around his wife.

"I learned a lot more about family these last few days," he said, "than I'd get from all the museums of Europe."

THE AUTHOR SAYS... **"Families can be so different, and we certainly drive each other crazy in my family, but there are some things that will always unite us."**

Out Of Step

A change of location can bring a change of perception – and set you back on the right track in your life again

By Francine Lee

he words had been said without thought. She had said them so often before when he had left her. It was what he expected to hear, although now she wondered whether it was what he actually *needed* to hear.

"I'll be fine," she had said when Alex kissed her lightly on the cheek before leaving for his meeting. Elizabeth had watched him stroll out of the hotel and into the streets of Merida and felt a sliver of fear run through her. She felt like a child on her first day at school.

Confidence had deserted her today. She had left it in the hotel room along with her sunglasses. It felt so strange after all this time, without him, without children to be responsible for. It had been years since she last had a few hours to fill, alone in another country.

Mexico was a surprise, not what she expected at all, and the Yucatan had a charm all of its own. The beauty and elegance of the French colonial buildings on the Paseo Montejo intrigued her.

It was so different to what she had imagined, a grace and refinement that stood out against the bustle of the city, cars streaming along the roads, horns honking.

She planned to spend the day exploring the Old Town while Alex attended a meeting. She had waited outside the hotel for the tour bus which allowed her to get on and off whenever she pleased at various points of interest around the city. She found a seat on the downstairs of the open-top bus to avoid squinting in the bright sunlight, irritated with herself for forgetting her sunglasses.

The tour passed through numerous avenues lined with elegant buildings, surrounded by lush greenery, until it turned to squeeze along the narrower streets that led to the Old Town.

Elizabeth got off the bus and joined the tourists that swelled the pavements

Elizabeth got off by the central square and joined the tourists thronging the pavements. She passed open-fronted shops, the doorways cluttered with vendors calling to her to come inside.

Continued overleaf...

ILLUSTRATIONS: THINKSTOCK, JIM DEWAR

She watched Alex stroll off down the street to his meeting

Continued from previous page

"No, gracias," she replied each time, still polite with her limited Spanish. Some stood and beckoned her in while others perched on small stools, allowing customers to decide for themselves.

A woman sat cradling a small baby, its hair dark and thick, not like the blond downy hair of her own babies so long ago. She felt a pang of wistfulness flicker within her.

The sun was climbing high in the sky now, the air becoming thick and still, and she sought momentary respite in the church on Calle 60. It was as busy as a shopping centre back home. Among those praying, heads bent, tourists wandered in and out of the stone pillars that held the wide expanse of the ceiling aloft, and her eyes were drawn to the huge crucifix dominating the altar.

A man in overalls and wielding a paint roller worked on regardless, freshening the cream paint at the entrance. Huge displays of lilies and greenery hung on the walls and an elderly gent sat on the back pew, poking a plastic stick between his teeth, wriggling it around with such vigour that Elizabeth was afraid it would damage his mouth. Inwardly she pleaded with him to stop.

She and Alex were so distant these days, so afraid of saying the wrong thing

She sought respite in the church

She sat for a while, watching the comings and goings. There was no rush, after all; for once she didn't have to consider the children or squeeze her own needs into the gaps in the day. She missed them desperately, but her mother was right; she needed time to herself – and time with Alex if they were to mend what was broken. Perhaps they needed a lick of paint, too.

Out in the open she strolled towards the central park, benches filled with couples entwined like octopuses. She noticed it wasn't limited to the young; older couples sat holding hands, or intimately close. It made her heart slip sideways. She and Alex were so distant these days, so afraid of saying or doing the wrong thing.

A chasm had grown between them that neither knew how to bridge.

She peered into doorways and saw barbers asleep in their chairs in the heat. Perspiration beaded her head and ran down her neck. Her mouth felt like an emery board and her eyes were beginning to tear up with the intensely bright sunlight.

She checked her watch. They had arranged to meet outside the Café Teatro but that would be a couple of hours yet. She wandered into the entrance of a small hotel, looking in the boutique windows that displayed linen clothes and sun hats. Deciding that a hat would be a welcome substitute for sunglasses, she went inside. With the help of the assistant, much gesticulation and broken language, both English and Spanish, she chose one with a wide brim that gave her the air of a reclusive movie star.

The assistant smiled approvingly. "Muy bueno, Senora, muy elegante."

She considered her reflection. How could a simple hat make so much difference to how she felt? She hesitated. It was the chance to be someone else. Someone confident and mysterious. She tilted her head to one side. No-one knew her, no-one could laugh and think her a fool. She could reinvent herself, be who she wanted to be – just for the day. She took out her purse and, refusing a bag, paid the assistant.

From inside the shop she could see through the glass doorway that led to the hotel interior. A cluster of tables were set among palms in an open courtyard – an oasis, and she needed a drink.

An elderly waiter in crisp white linen slipped over to her, beaming, his teeth a brilliant white to match his uniform. She ordered coffee and a bottle of water and looked up, glimpsing the sky between palm fronds. The breeze whispered through them and water trickled over a fountain in the centre, bubbling over a carved stone bowl.

She settled herself at a table that looked out through the doorway she had entered by, watching the passing traffic.

The waiter reappeared, smoothed the white linen tablecloth flat and placed a small vase of flowers on the table before disappearing as silently as he came.

She felt like a treasured guest

She could hear doors open and close in distant rooms, maids moving slowly about the corridors, the slow tick-tock of their brooms across the cool tiled floor, and she eased back into her chair and closed her eyes for a moment.

The coffee arrived in a small glass pot accompanied by a jug of frothy milk. The waiter placed her cup and saucer before her and bowed, leaving her with the sensation that she was a treasured guest.

She was the only customer. It was the rainy season, she recalled, looking up to the sky. Was it sensible to sit here?

A liveried receptionist glimpsed her from the reception desk. He had her

Continued overleaf...

Continued from previous page
down as a mad Englishwoman, she supposed. Clouds gathered overhead and the breeze swept through the palms.

The silence was punctuated by light thuds as oranges were blown to the ground. The juice seeped onto the tiles and Elizabeth watched it trickle like sweat into the gaps between the stone tiles of the courtyard.

She liked this slower pace of life, away from laptops and smart phones.

She poured herself another cup. No need to rush. No need to step back into the heat, into life, just yet.

Things had moved so fast lately; Alex's promotion, the children becoming more independent. She had been groundless, unable to make decisions. Should she go back to work? She would have to retrain, of course, she expected that. Or should she keep herself flexible, available to go with Alex on his travels?

She felt out of step somehow, unable to get back in the dance of life again. And Alex, so busy with his new position, new responsibilities, had no time for her dithering, her indecision.

Did he understand how she really felt? He seemed so removed from what he had been. Their lives seemed out of kilter. One was moving ahead and the other trailing behind, flailing helplessly, and he hadn't seemed to notice.

Draining the coffee pot, she sat for a while then made her way to meet Alex.

She found herself a bench and waited in the shade of jacaranda trees. It wasn't long before she saw him striding through the crowds, tall and elegant in his short-sleeved shirt, his sunglasses.

Her heart fluttered a little with expectation as his face broke into a smile when he saw her. She couldn't remember the last time he'd smiled at her like that, or the last time she'd noticed. Perhaps it was her hat, or perhaps it was she who hadn't been paying attention.

Alex kissed her cheek and she could smell his lemon-scented aftershave. He stood back and admired her.

"You look wonderful. I love your hat. Have you been alright?"

She was about to reply that she was fine but stopped herself, simply nodded.

"Shall we take a walk?" He held out his arm and she took it.

She felt heady with the heat, her senses jumbled. Alex was different, alert, charged with an energy she hadn't noticed before. His delight in seeing her was not forced in any way and suddenly she was disorientated.

She was disorientated. Had it been she who created the distance between them?

Had it been she who had created this distance between them? Or was he energised because he was enjoying his work and she was here with him, no distractions, nothing to do but enjoy each other? She gripped his arm tighter and he turned and smiled at her again.

"Good meeting?"

He nodded. "Excellent."

He rattled off the main details as they wandered back the way she had already travelled. "Let's eat first, then I'll show you the Old Town."

"I've been exploring it," she said, hesitating, aware she could break the new

Alex drew her close

understanding between them.

"Ah, but that's the afternoon. Things will be all change now that it's Friday night." He smiled indulgently as they were directed to a table.

When they finally stepped out of the restaurant the streets were sectioned off by barriers, cars being diverted by smart policemen. The noise from a distant square was beginning to fill the air, voices raised in laughter and whoops of delight.

Alex led her onwards, a protective arm about her waist as they squeezed through the crowds milling in the street.

Elizabeth felt she had gone from one world into another in a matter of hours. Mexico was a constant unfolding mystery, neither one thing nor another. Whatever you thought it was to begin with could change in the blink of an eye.

Stages were set up in alleyways and courtyards, lights strung across the streetlamps glowing faintly in the late sunshine, and it seemed to Elizabeth that there were a dozen different kinds of music all being played at the same time.

They stopped and watched two clowns performing to a crowd that burst periodically into laughter.

Alex shrugged. "Must lose something in translation," he laughed as they moved on.

They weaved through the crowds towards the church where she had stopped earlier. Now there was a stage, a band performing; people filled the pavements and spilled onto the streets, dancing where they stood, unafraid, unselfconscious, and their freedom was infectious. It was difficult to ignore the rhythms which seemed to reverberate from every surface and she began to sway in time to it, stepping to the side and back again.

Alex watched approvingly, his smile breaking the wrinkles at his eyes, and she felt light and lithe, glad to be with him.

Then Alex moved closer, held out his hands, pulled her into the crowd, drawing her close to him and letting her go again. They smiled at each other, smiled to those around them, and Elizabeth felt true happiness for the first time in years.

They were in step again, and she remembered her earlier words of the morning. Everything would be fine.

They moved in time to the music, in step with each other once more.

"I was lucky enough to have a wonderful holiday in Mexico and was fascinated by how the city reinvented itself at the weekend, work stopped and the party began in the streets."

A Second Genesis

We have all the time in the world – don't we? But the world is running out of time, and we must act now – or never

By Rose Layland

his is not a punishment, Jonka, but a remedy. You have been regressing. It happens to those who have too long a contact with the human tribe. The ancient emotions can still be active in spite of eons of conditioning. Because you are a scientist working with our community of humans you have become involved with them in an emotional way.

"Humans are emotional creatures – the very reason why they have destroyed their planet. They gave way to impulses without the discipline of reason. Their greed and indifference destroyed their habitat, although they were warned well in advance by their own scientists."

Jonka listened patiently while the Master recited facts which were elementary to him. The Master was an organiser but liked to impress his scientists with his intimate knowledge of all aspects of the universe.

"They would have been destroyed totally if we had not discovered a small tribe of them huddled in an area where natural life still remained.

"And what did we do? We brought them to the Mother Planet and safety. We provided them with conditions especially manufactured to accord with those of their own planet. We allowed them to live and to breed in that haphazard way of theirs, passing their own weaknesses and wilfulness into their young.

"But for all our care, they yearn always for their own world. They lived in misery, fear and discontent, and yet their descendants would exchange all our security and ordered tranquillity for their

ILLUSTRATIONS: THINKSTOCK, MANDY DIXON

old life. Emotion, you see." He shook his head, making his wattles tremble.

"They are a project. We monitor their world for its recovery. Then, and only then, can we return them. So you see, by sending you on this important work you will, in some small way, be contributing to their return.

"And the time spent away from the Mother Planet will allow you space to think, to regulate yourself and remove yourself from the influence of Lucy and her family. You will be able to see first hand the desolation that their forebears created out of a perfect planet.

"That should be enough to show you the danger of putting anything before science and truth."

As the Master's voice murmured on, Jonka recalled the occasion he had tried to persuade Lucy to accept the implant that would allow her, like himself, to live forever. She had been horrified.

"What?" she had cried. "And become as robotic as you? You were raised in a laboratory, genetically modified and then programmed. What sort of life is it if you do not live with passion, marry, have children, know excitement, yearning, the pain of living? These things bring meaning to life – colour. They *are* life."

He had watched her vehemence calmly.

"Lucy. Your kind is as we once were. But then we found that these things you cling to squandered our energies. There was another way. We would lose certain things, but our planet would be safe-guarded. We had no alternative than to grasp scientific breakthroughs, cloning, medical enlightenment, cosmic energy."

But Lucy had been outraged. "You do not live," she'd cried. "You exist."

Then her quick spirit had relented and she'd put a soothing hand on his arm.

"Jonka, I did not mean to hurt you. You are my friend. My good friend. But just look at you all – moving through time on an endless plateau, wallowing in your science and smug philosophies."

"You will see first-hand the desolation they created out of a perfect planet"

Jonka, as always, was patient. "All life is a progress. Time taught us that, through science and rational thought, we could safeguard our planet. No planet means no life. Do you not want to return to your Earth?"

Continued overleaf...

Continued from previous page

Lucy had paused, her colour subsiding. At length she'd said hesitantly, "I don't know. I am afraid. I know only of it from the stories handed down by our forebears. Yet it is where we belong."

Semonoids do not smile, but Jonka was conscious of warmth as he responded, "Humans seek always for happiness. It is like trying to reach the horizon and finding there is a further horizon. Your spirits are restless and discontented.

"Because of the brevity of your lives you are in haste to seize, to devour before you die. But if you lived forever, your focus would change. I beg you, Lucy, allow us to do this for you."

Jonka had left her to think about it, but he knew that the very qualities she would lose were those that held her back from taking the step he proposed.

He was given no opportunity to see Lucy before he went into exile. He knew he would never see her again; perhaps her children's children's children, but not Lucy. He would be away too long. The journey itself was an age.

He occupied himself usefully between his trance-like sleeps, studying through the monitors the condition of the red, hazy planet with its dust storms and high winds, its spread of sludge which had once been seas.

He studied the historical records of bountiful provisions, creatures that had flourished within its manifold habitats. It was difficult to comprehend how a leading species could be so stupid, so egotistical as to believe that they could please themselves and not bring disaster down on their heads. Their history suggested they had fought long and hard for their freedoms and, having gained them, forgot that with freedom comes responsibility.

The Master was right; the legacy of humans was their own disaster.

They had never learned by their mistakes. They blundered about through their short lives, creating chaos out of natural order. They used most of the brilliance of their scientists for the destruction of one another or of the natural balance of their planet. They were such a primitive form of life.

As the ship came down into the complex which had been designed and constructed to shield his species from this alien habitat, he was decontaminated and taken to the cell which was to become his home.

Instructions were fed to him as to how the monitors and records worked, and he was soon into the routine of his new world. He did not feel the isolation too much – his species were used to working alone in a sphere of technology and robots – on the contrary, he relished the lack of distraction, the ability to concentrate wholly on his mission.

Painstakingly he traced the history of the Earth from records handed down by humans, their painful journey from ancient man to what they had called civilisation. He familiarised himself with areas which had once been territories, the old boundaries of sea and land, the rhythms of the climates and the dramatic changes which had happened with such haste that life had not been able to adapt and had been overwhelmed.

He visited old records which showed how it had once appeared, rich and vibrant scenes from the icelands to what had been called jungles.

He saw images of amazing creatures and astounding plants. Each species had provided nutrients and nourishment for others. Nothing had been wasted. Everything had been softened and dissolved to give nourishment to the earth. Pollution had been seized and purified by the organics which had operated on every level. A perfect world.

What had they done? But Jonka was a scientist. No energy was wasted on censure or sadness. Men had been created and were imperfect. So be it. But they must have been very powerful to convert such a verdant paradise into a poisoned wasteland.

Jonka settled into a routine of steady monitoring. Each period found him scanning the surface of the earth. His monitor allowed him to record weather patterns and disturbances, tremors beneath the planet's crust.

He compared all with previous readings, looking for a pattern of change. It might not happen now, it might not happen in an eon, but there would come a time when it would happen. The earth would cleanse itself.

But only after Lucy was long gone.

Humans measured something they called time, but for Semonoids, as beings who lived forever, there were only ages, cosmic happenings.

For long periods Jonka went into a torpor in which he rested through his long vigil and slept away a human's century. During his wake-times he became aware of shifting changes in his records. There was a reduction in the ferocity of storms, periods when the dust thinned and settled, bringing an increase in light. Then his monitor found traces of vapour above an old mountain.

It might not happen in an eon, but the Earth would cleanse itself in time

Systematically he explored his charts and made calculations.

There was no doubt of it. The earth's rages were dying. He plotted each portion of the globe, noting the imperceptible growth of ice at the two extremities. The sun appeared, a round red disc between banks of dust clouds, and daily temperatures increased.

The vapours became more significant and he turned his attention towards small

Continued overleaf...

Continued from previous page

pockets of the Earth's surface where once had grown huge, rich plants. Furiously he back-tracked until he found what he sought. A fragile stem had looped upwards, bearing two delicate lobes of green which spread and enlarged towards the light.

The long metamorphosis had begun.

He relayed the findings to the Mother Planet. Lucy's descendants would be informed. How would they react? Bred in their alien home, perhaps the news would have little impact on them. Would they want to return to a habitat about which they had only heard stories?

Over time he traced an increase in seedling growth, some gaining height and flourishing, some dying. He dispatched data as he gathered it, and there came additional traffic from the Mother Planet bearing more scientists, more supplies.

When Jonka saw her coming towards him down the corridor of monitors, his immediate reaction was that there was some failure of his senses brought about by the long periods of solitude. Lucy had faded into the back of his consciousness, and all his work had been for the benefit of her descendants.

Yet as the figure continued to approach he saw clearly the vision of his old friend. She stood before him and he saw that Lucy was completely unchanged, save for her placid movements and the calmness which had replaced the old vitality in her face, a face which she turned up to gaze into his lizard's eyes.

"Jonka." Her voice was as of old. "You remember me?"

There was the familiar lilt of teasing in it. The Master had been right; he had regressed, it was still there and the sight of her brought that familiar warmth to him. He'd had to learn her language to communicate, but now she addressed him in his tongue.

His dear friend had harkened to him after all. He held out one leathery hand in the manner of her people and she covered it quickly with her own.

"See, Jonka." She parted her hair on the crown of her head and showed him the scar. "I took the implant and it was a success. I studied your language, and I became a scientist. The Master let me come. I think his eyes almost twinkled. Perhaps he is regressing, too." Again the faint teasing lilt. "He says we will work well together. If you will have me, that is. Are you content?"

Contentment was the nearest thing a Semonoid could get to happiness, and Jonka was very content.

He led her along to the cell and showed her the infant forest. "Come, Lucy. We have much work to do. It has begun."

Teatime Treat

Flower Fondant Fancies

Ingredients

- 3 large eggs
- 80g caster sugar
- 80g plain flour
- 25g butter, melted
- 3-4tbsp raspberry or strawberry jam

Decoration:

- 400g icing sugar
- Pink and blue food colouring
- Green and white writing icing
- Small icing flowers
- Icing ladybirds (optional)

1 Preheat oven to 190°C, Fan Oven 170°C, Gas Mark 5. Grease a 23cm square cake tin and line base with greaseproof paper.

2 Whisk the eggs and sugar with a hand-held electric mixer on high speed for 4-5min, until very thick and pale in colour.

3 Fold in flour with a large metal spoon, then gently stir in cooled melted butter. Transfer to tin and spread out. Bake for 25-30min until firm. Cool. Remove paper.

4 Cut cake in half lengthways, trim edges and sandwich together with jam. Cut into 8 squares.

5 Mix icing sugar with 4tbsp cold water. Divide between 2 basins, adding 1-2 drops pink colouring to one and blue to the other. Ice the cakes. Leave to set.

6 Decorate cakes with green icing to make stems, white icing to make bows, then fix icing flowers and ladybirds onto the cakes with a little icing.

RECIPE: SUE ASHWORTH PHOTOGRAPHY: NATHAN KING

Up In The Gallery...

Marie Lloyd, sweetheart of the music hall and theatre, charms the audience – and one young man in particular...

By Donald Lightwood

You could feel the audience's anticipation as Marie Lloyd reached the last song in her act. It had made her famous and placed her at the top of the bill in all of London's music halls. Everybody knew the words.

The boy I love is up in the gallery, the boy I love is looking now at me...

As you would expect, she directed the words up to the theatre gallery. *There he is, can't you see...* prompting the men to respond as she sang. *Waving his handkerchief...*

She was exhausted when she finally came offstage after the inevitable encore.

"Did you see the Standard, Marie? It says 1914's been our best year yet!"

The Pavilion manager met her in the wings. He was holding a newspaper.

"Did you see the Standard tonight, Marie?" he asked her.

"Can't say I did."

He had the paper open at the show page. "It says here 1914's been our best year yet," he announced. "Thanks to our own dear Marie."

"That mean I'm due a rise, then?" she asked.

He laughed. "Always the comic," he told her, re-folding the paper.

There was a large headline on the front page. *WAR DECLARED.*

As a top ranking artiste, Marie Lloyd had her own dressing room. She cherished this mark of her success more than anything else. She'd been in the business for over thirty years and had to share for many of them.

She opened the first of two bottles of stout. This was medicinal, for her throbbing vocal cords. The second, she told herself, was her reward for all the hard work on the boards.

There was a knock on the door.

"Come in, if you're sober!" she called out loudly.

The door opened slowly, revealing a handsome young man clutching his cap in his hands.

"Who are you, then?" Marie asked.

He stared at her open-mouthed.

Continued overleaf...

ILLUSTRATIONS: THINKSTOCK, JAMES DEWAR

Marie mesmerised the audience every night

A handsome young man entered her dressing room

Continued from previous page

"Well?" She took a swing of stout.

The young man swallowed and made himself speak.

"...I'm the boy you love," he said.

"You what?"

"Up in the gallery."

She snorted, spilling some stout. "That's a good one, that is. What you really here for?"

He hesitated, twisting his cap.

"I come every night and you always point at me."

"Don't be daft," she told him. "I point at all the lads up there."

"No you don't. I'm always in the same seat and you always pick me out."

She topped up her glass, concentrating on it, rather than him. "I can't even see you when I'm on the stage."

"I can see you," he said.

"Course you can," she retorted. "That's what it's all about."

He edged a little further into the room. Marie sat up in her chair, on her guard.

"You're the only girl I've ever loved," he told her breathlessly.

She gave out a yelp.

"Girl! Blimey, that's a good one, that is." She laughed out loud. "Want a bet? I bet I'm old enough to be your mother."

"I don't care."

"How old are you?"

"Nineteen."

"I was right," she cried. "I could have had you and half a dozen more."

"I still love you," he protested.

She took off the flowered headdress she always wore on stage.

"No, you don't. You've fallen in love with the woman I pretend to be. Like all the other blokes."

He stood in silence, the look on his face reminding her of her dog when she wouldn't take him out.

She went on. "It's the name of the game – music hall, the theatre. Illusion. We're a dream factory."

"I know that," he answered quietly.

"Well, then."

"I'm different," he said.

"It doesn't sound like it," she replied.

"I've lost count how many times I've seen you," he said. "I know I love you."

She shook her head, irritated, and pointed at the greasepaint and powder on her dressing table.

"See them? They're my tools. Without them I'd be nothing." She looked in the mirror. "See that pretty face? I'll show you what's under it."

She spread removing cream on her face and rubbed it off with a towel. The evocative smell filled the room.

Naturally, being Marie, she exaggerated. For a forty-four-year-old woman her face was a little worn, but still acceptable.

"See – the old battleaxe. Now don't you go telling anybody else what you've seen tonight."

"You're still lovely," he said.

"You need specs, duck," she replied, peering at herself in the mirror. "I'll tell you something else. I am not a good woman. I've been divorced, lived in sin, and I drink too much. The lot." She stopped and turned sharply to face him. "Why am I telling you all this?"

A slight smile had crept onto his face.

She glanced away, but could still see his reflection in the mirror.

In her mind she answered her own question. *Because it can't go on forever.* Pretending to be the cheeky fresh faced young girl who had won audiences over the years. She'd become two people. Seemingly it still worked. But for how much longer?

"How did you get in here, anyway?" she demanded.

"I waited till the others had gone and the doorkeeper was stuck in his newspaper."

"You'd better go." She shook out her hair. "This is supposed to be my happy time, not making my confession."

He handed her a picture postcard from his pocket.

"Will you sign this for me, please?"

"Stone the crows," she said, looking at an early photograph of herself. "That's me, about your age."

"It's beautiful."

She smiled. "That girl really had something. What's your name?"

He gasped when he read what she had written.

To Alfred, with much love from Marie. I won't forget you.

She held up her hand. "Before you get carried away, that's from her up on the stage," she told him. "Understood?"

He nodded and put on his cap.

"I think I'll go now, Marie."

"It's the name of the game – the music hall. Illusion. We're a dream factory"

After the show a few days later, Marie was on her second bottle of stout when the manager came into her dressing room.

"Sorry about the rumpus in the gallery after your last number," he told her.

"What was the trouble?" she asked.

"You, in a way." He grinned. "It seems one of the punters was boasting about how you'd told him you loved him. He'd

Continued overleaf...

Continued from previous page

had a drink, of course. Anyway some of the lads decided to sort him out."

"Men," she said, pulling a face. "I thought he was a bit different. Nothing changes."

"That's where you're wrong, my dear." He dropped a piece of sheet music on the table in front of her.

"What's this?"

"A new number – you'll be doing it all week."

"Hang on," she said. "I'm the one who chooses what I sing."

"Not when General Kitchener's about, you don't," he told her. "It's Marie Lloyd's contribution to the War Effort."

The Pavilion Theatre was decked out in red, white and blue bunting for the following night's performance.

After she'd sung her last number, Marie was joined on stage by the company waving flags and a Recruiting Sergeant.

"This song is specially for all the young chaps here tonight," cried Marie. Her patriotic words filled the house.

"*We don't want to lose you,*
But we think you ought to go.
Your King and Country
Both need you so."

The audience cheered and after an encore, the Recruiting Sergeant spoke up.

"Now lads, you heard what the lady said, and she's dead right. Step up here and take the King's Shilling and you'll get a kiss from the lovely Marie Lloyd."

The band played and men were urged forward by their wives and sweethearts. A queue of volunteers formed down the aisle and up onto the stage.

Marie dutifully kissed the young men, who mostly appeared to be struck dumb with the emotion of the moment.

There was one exception. Alfred. He stood in front of Marie with a black eye. She couldn't help a giggle.

"I still love you, Marie," he said.

"Course you do, ducks."

"No, I mean it," he went on. "You changed my life. I was nobody, but now I'm somebody."

"Come on, give us a kiss," she said. "My hero," she added as they parted.

"Honest?"

"I haven't never had no blokes have a scrap over me before."

"Get moving there!" shouted the Sergeant. "We've got a war to win."

"I love both of you," he called over his shoulder as he marched away.

She gave him a knowing smile and then faced up to the next volunteer, prepared to do her duty.

THE AUTHOR SAYS...

"The 44-year-old Marie Lloyd really did perform at the Pavilion Theatre in August, 1914. An example of how the music hall helped recruitment can be seen in the film *Oh! What A Lovely War.*"

Fancy That!

Fascinating **Winter flower** facts!

◆ **The chrysanthemum is the birth flower of people born in November.**

◆ Bouquets containing only red and white flowers are considered bad luck.

◆ **The ancient Romans believed holly warded off lightning strikes and witchcraft.**

◆ The earliest known flower arrangers were the ancient Egyptians, around 2500 BC.

It's said that if an unmarried girl is kissed under the mistletoe, then the mistletoe is burned, she will get married

◆ The world's oldest fossilised flower bloomed 125 million years ago.

◆ **Sarcococca are a group of plants known as "Christmas box".**

Forget-me-not is the state flower of Alaska

◆ **Pigsqueak, elephant's ears and large rockfoil are all names for bergenia.**

◆ Narcissus is the birth flower of people born in December.

Hellebore is nicknamed the Christmas rose

The poinsettia is the flower of Christmas Eve

◆ The witch in witch-hazel comes from the Middle English word wiche, meaning pliant or bendable.

◆ **Wintersweet is known as the ice flower in Iran.**

◆ Sixty gardens took part in Scotland's first Snowdrop Festival in 2007.

WORDS: DOUGLAS MACPHERSON PICTURES: THINKSTOCK

Jeepers, Creepers!

A lovely, bewitching lady and an encounter with a terrifying creature – this story is sure to send shivers up your spine

By Karen Byrom

"Anyone fancy going to a Hallowe'en party this weekend?" Nick asked cheerfully as he entered the crowded staff room just before the bell rang for the end of afternoon break.

"Not a chance!" Megan, Year Six's hard-pressed teacher, rolled her eyes. "I have enough dealings with little devils in my classroom all year round."

"Nor me," Val concurred. "By the time my demons in Year Five have had their afternoon party, I'll only be fit for bed."

"What about you, Ellie?" Nick asked the infant class mistress. "Are you up for a night of ghosties and ghoulies, et cetera?" he asked.

"Not me!" Ellie laughed. "Not if there are going to be 'long-leggedy beasties' about. I hate spiders." She gave a mock shudder. "Besides, I don't mind indulging the little ones by dressing up as a witch for their party but by Friday night, I'll be too tired to be out and about on my broomstick. It's an early night for me."

She didn't notice Nick's face fall as she crossed over to the sink to rinse her cup.

Ever since the youngest member of staff had joined St Paul's at the beginning of the school year, the deputy head had been bewitched by her soft brown eyes, burnished brown hair and beautiful figure. He'd been looking for an excuse to ask her out and Hallowe'en had seemed the ideal opportunity. And now she'd turned him down.

Ellie sighed as she gathered up the scraps of black and orange tissue paper her five-year-olds had scattered all over the floor as they excitedly made creepy collages to decorate the classroom walls. She loved her job – her first one since qualifying – but it certainly left her tired out by the end of the day.

"After the kids' party I'll be too tired to be out and about on my broomstick!"

She thought again about Nick's invitation. When did she last go to a party, or even have a night out? Maybe she should have taken him up on it.

But, she reminded herself hastily, the invitation wasn't really to her – he'd thrown it out to the whole room. If he'd asked her, and her alone – well, her answer might have been different. She'd

ILLUSTRATIONS: MANDY DIXON, THINKSTOCK

liked the deputy head on first meeting him at her initial interview, and nothing had happened to change her mind since. He was unfailingly polite and helpful – as well as being possessed of a headful of springy black curls, dancing blue eyes, and a wicked sense of humour.

A Hallowe'en party with him as a partner would have been fun…

Jason, the black cat that belonged to the school janitor, stretched himself lazily as he got down from the comfy armchair where he'd been snoozing in the corner of the staffroom. His tail twitched and his green eyes glinted as he nosed his way around the door.

He padded along the corridor, silent

Continued overleaf...

Continued from previous page

now that the last bell had rung and children excited about Hallowe'en had skipped their way out of the school gates, dropping gloves and scarves and empty lunchboxes as they clutched their more precious cargo of pipe-cleaner spiders, paper masks and cardboard witches' hats.

Jason's nose twitched as he picked up the smell he'd been looking for – the faint trace of pomegranate and lime that the new infant teacher's perfume always left in her wake. He stopped by a door, ears a-twitch, listening to the sounds of chairs being righted and papers stacked in order, and the occasional heartfelt sigh of a pretty girl suddenly aware in her empty classroom that after caring for twenty children all day, she had no-one at home to care for her.

Along the corridor, Jason stopped once more outside a second door, to pick up the murmur of a one-sided telephone conversation as the deputy head placated a parent with questions about their child.

Right… time for a quick trip to the basement to call in some favours.

The screams that echoed around the corridors of St Paul's Primary School would have sent a lesser man than Nick running for the outside door. But recognising Ellie's normally dulcet tones, he charged down the corridor instead, bursting into her classroom to tackle whatever demon lurked there.

He looked round wildly but there was nothing to be seen except Ellie, perched precariously on top of a small desk, her whole body shaking as she pointed to the floor.

"Get it out! Get rid of it!" she cried.

Nick looked down. A little black spider – a real, live, proper spider, not one made of pipe-cleaners – skittered around the legs of the desk.

Before he could bend to pick it up, Jason appeared, lazily batted the spider with his paw and chased it from the room.

Ellie collapsed into Nick's arms, almost sobbing with relief.

"Oh, thank you. I really do hate spiders. I thought it was one the children had made and I – " she gulped – " I actually went to pick it up. I *touched* it!"

She looked up at him, expecting him to laugh. But his eyes were kind and his grip around her comforting as he whispered soothing words into her ear.

As Ellie rested her head on Nick's shoulder, two black shapes – one cat-sized, one spider-sized – strolled together down the corridor before going their separate ways. One to the basement, where she and her family lived in peace thanks to Jason's pacific nature; the other to the warmth of the janitor's hearth rug.

If cats and spiders could high-five, they would have. Their Hallowe'en work was done.

THE AUTHOR SAYS… **"Brought up on tales of Robert the Bruce, spiders have always seem quite benevolent to me and I liked the idea of one of them doing a good deed."**

Teatime Treat

Fresh Strawberry Pops

Ingredients

- **12 large whole strawberries**
- **50g each pink and dark chocolate**
- **75g white chocolate**
- **2tbsp toasted flaked almonds, crushed**
- **2tbsp desiccated coconut**

1 Wash and pat dry the strawberries and skewer with lolly sticks or skewers. Line a board with baking parchment.

2 Break all the chocolate into pieces and place in separate bowls. Melt over saucepans of barely simmering water. Remove from the water.

3 Carefully dip 4 strawberries in each of the chocolates to coat, and place on the lined board. Sprinkle almonds over the dark chocolate and coconut over the white before the chocolate sets. Put in a cool place to set.

4 To finish, re-melt any remaining white chocolate and drizzle over the pink covered strawberries. Leave to set before serving.

RECIPE: KATHRYN HAWKINS PHOTOGRAPHY: STUART MACGREGOR

The Hand Of Fate

The prophecy of my power was disturbing – yet surely it was merely the utterance of a fairground charlatan?

By H Johnson-Mack

The woman who said that I had it in my power to change the course of history was nothing special to look upon. Her face would never launch ships; her hair was the richest thing about her, yet all but lost within the folds of a threadbare mantle. She wore rings of ruby glass; that I did note. But then, it was a fashion of her trade and thus became as unremarkable as the rest of her, to be forgotten in a few hours, if not for what she'd predicted.

It was at the Aylsham fayre of 1507 that I saw her. Always an exciting occasion, and today the heavens had blessed us with fine weather to enhance our morsel of freedom from the daily grind.

Not that I was unhappy. The manor house where I served as maid was prosperous, not as rich as the master's main residence, but still a lovely place to live. When I thought of my sisters stuck in the bogs of my birthplace, the land of perpetual skies, I was glad to be here. My fellows were a good crowd, with only the odd cruel streak and wandering hands to avoid as in any society, and the housekeeper not so strict that you couldn't so much as breathe without earning a scold.

The lord we served was obsessed with making his way in King Harry's court, which could only bode well for his servants if he was successful. His lady was a noble rung on that ladder, and the children a lively lot who always brought a smile to my face whenever I was sent to mind them. But I was young, then, and still fresh enough to love a break from the normal routine.

There was so much to see of the fayre before we were due back at the Hall that I hesitated to waste precious minutes and a silver coin on having my fortune told.

I hesitated to waste precious minutes and a coin on having my fortune told

"But you must, Tilly," my fellow maid Bet insisted. "It could bring you luck."

So with a sigh, I went into the tiny tent she had just emerged from.

Continued overleaf...

Continued from previous page

Inside, it was black as night; the only light came from a poor smoking lamp at the feet of a shrouded figure, its fumes adding to the fetid air within.

"Do you wish to learn what your future holds?"

The teller had spoken without moving an inch on the stool where she sat, before another set ready for customers.

I gulped and answered, "Aye," and was waved solemnly to the empty seat.

"Then sit, my dear, and cross my palm with coin."

A hand was extended. I did as I was bidden, stealing a glance at the hooded gypsy as I sat. The shadows hid most of her from me, but I could just glimpse a face almost as young as mine amongst a riot of ebony curls. As soon as the coin was pocketed, she seized my hand, turning it down toward the failing light.

"I see love in your lines," she intoned after a moment's examination, her voice low and lyrical. "A babe or two, if you follow your heart. And long life, where health rewards a good soul."

I almost laughed aloud. Why, she could have been reciting lines from a play, she sounded so rehearsed! Suddenly, I saw the gypsy for what she really was; a wandering player, employing shadow and superstition to earn her daily meal. And good luck to her, but I could no longer take her seriously.

"Thank you, mistress," said I, a laugh in my voice. "I'll be sure to bear it in mind."

"Wait!"

The cry was abrupt, the hand on my wrist a vice as she prevented me from rising. She stared, unblinking, for an uncomfortable moment before she said urgently, "You must beware, young maid! For you have the power to topple kings and bring down towers. I have seen it."

The cry was abrupt, the hand on my wrist a vice as she stopped me rising

She did not speak again, and I took my leave of her hastily, glad beyond reason to be back out in the soothing sunshine with the merry song of folk at leisure filling my ears.

"What did she say?" demanded Bet as soon as I emerged.

"Oh, the usual," I replied, wondering if the young teller was actually a little mad, or else I had offended her pride by my chuckles so she'd sought to frighten me with words. "You know, 'handsome stranger, happy-ever-after'."

The end of this sentence became a squeal as my backside was heartily pinched. I whirled round to look into the laughing face of the Hall's head groom.

"Handsome stranger, you say? Well, here I am, me darlin'!"

"Get you gone, Tom O'Hallon!" I cried. But I was half-hearted in chasing him off, for he was in his way as exotic as the gypsy with his dark Irish looks and island blood, and I wasn't averse to a little flirting with him.

The months passed, season into season, and I forgot all about the fortune-teller. Yuletide came and went – a merry time, with the mistress presiding quietly over all as she recovered from the birth of another babe to ease the pain of those lost to Heaven, and O'Hallon stealing my kisses under the mistletoe. Winter was upon us, and the shortened days were mostly spent by warm hearths whenever the opportunity arose.

But not all sought the fires. Some would much rather be out amongst the frozen boughs and sleeping meadows, finding ways to play even in that cold and unforgiving landscape. So it was with my lady's children. And on this day, it was I who was charged with minding them.

We romped in the woodlands, playing hide and seek and spot-the-berry in a frost-world of white. The two girls were a delight; handsome and engaging, the younger the most vibrant, with a quick mind and sharp wit glistening in her merry black eyes. She was the hardest to keep in check, even when the young master grew up enough to join in their games and they became a close trio. She it was who drove them to adventure, and their minders to distraction trying to mould them into nobility.

So I was not surprised to find that it was this one who, after failing to awaken hibernating bunnies, sought a bigger thrill. She determined to skate across the lake in naught but her slippers, and of course, her elder sister would not be left behind. I tried to reason with them, without success. I was left to meekly follow as they abandoned their sturdy pattens by the water's edge.

It was cold, yea, but not so numbing as it had been, and the sun had been our constant companion for some days. Perhaps that was why the ice was not as thick as previously. Or perhaps something more sinister was at work that day. Whatever the reason, when my little mistress went boldly out across the lake, I could see the thinner centre reflected in the sun, and cracks in the ice perilously close to her feet. I immediately cried a warning. Giggling, she turned to throw an impish look over her shoulder. Then her laughter died as she felt the ice give way.

"Tilly!" she screamed as she slipped and fell heavily. "Help me!"

I was already on my way, easing on my knees across the ice. The screams of both girls rang in my ears, along with my own frantic heartbeat. But I instinctively knew I must go slowly; ignore the urgent desire to fly toward the body lying treacherously close to the gaping hole. For if I moved too fast, the ice would break, the little mistress would be pitched into the lake's freezing depths, her clothes dragging her down – and I could not swim...

If I moved too fast, the little mistress would be pitched into the icy depths

It seemed to take forever to cross just yards. As careful as I'd been, there was

Continued overleaf...

Continued from previous page

still an ominous crack and surface shift as my body drew near to the hole. I watched as, in slow motion, Mistress's slippers disappeared, then her legs.

"Tilly!"she cried. I flung myself forward, reaching out a desperate arm to stop her falling. "Take my hand!" I screamed. "Grab it, quickly!"

For one horrific moment, I thought she wasn't going to do it. I thought that she was going to let the waters take her, pull her under to her death. Then she twisted, kicked and snatched at my hand. There was a second when our palms slipped, then I grabbed hold of those frozen little fingers and held on for grim death.

Our eyes met across the ice; mine desperate, hers determined and of a wisdom way beyond her tender years. Then I was hauling with all my strength and inching backward at the same time, repeating "Hold on, hold on," over and over as I heard her sister running for help.

By the time it came, I'd managed to slide far enough from the thin ice to keep us safe, but it was with heartfelt relief that I released my little mistress into the stronger, warmer arms of a manservant.

She was soaked through, but she was alive. At the time, though I was personally commended by my lady for my actions, all I really cared about was getting warm again.

It is only now, when my life is all but done, and I have the wisdom of time to look back upon, that I can see just how true the teller spoke all those years ago.

I did find love, in the form of my Irish groom, who in due course made me Mrs O'Hallon and took me away to his island for hard, happy years until his death and my desire to return to my homelands, with the two children he had given me.

And I was content, and of late, anticipating going to meet him again, when the momentous events of the time intrude upon my peace to remind me of the gypsy and her prediction.

She had been right, that young ruby-ringed wanderer. I, a lowly serving maid, did indeed have a chance to divert the course of history.

And I ask myself, if I had known then what I know now, how one simple act would later contribute to the toppling of a nation's chief beliefs, the death of a thousand priories… would I still have done again what I did? Or would I have allowed that foolhardy little girl to drown?

For my bold black-eyed mistress grew up to possess the power to bewitch no less than a king – a king who would change a whole country's religion in order for him to marry her.

And her name was Anne Boleyn…

I ask myself: had I known then what I know now, would I have saved her?

THE AUTHOR SAYS… **"Have you ever wondered how history could have turned out differently if just one moment in time hadn't happened? Thinking over that question is how this story came about."**

BRAIN BOOSTERS SOLUTIONS

CODEWORD from page 29

PHRASE: VIOLETS ARE BLUE

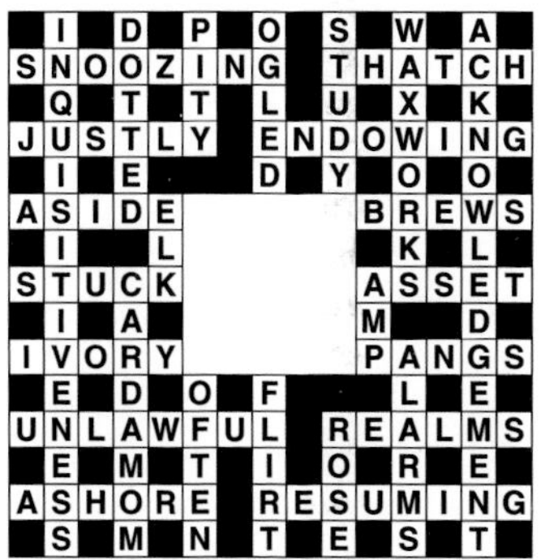

KRISS KROSS from page 51

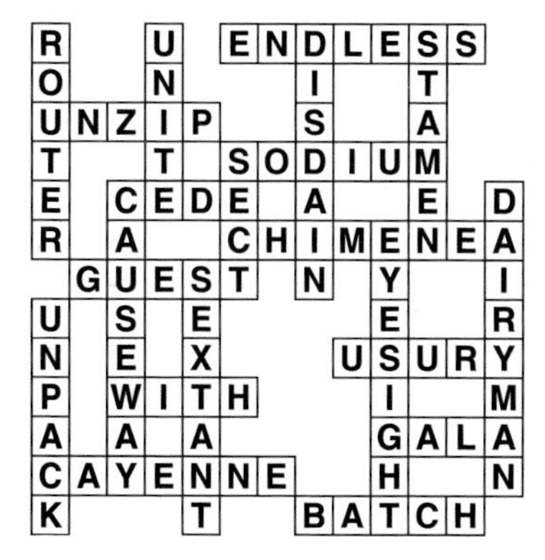

MISSING LINK from Page 95

ACROSS: 2 Group 7 Year 8 Coin 9 Top 10 Grouse 11 Points 13 Cards 14 Runner 15 Gas 16 Bubble 18 Cross 21 Sponge 23 Regent 25 Rub 26 Barn 27 Text 28 Lines **DOWN:** 1 Rear 2 Ground 3 Outer 4 Peppers 5 Action 6 Pint 12 Sores 13 Cubes 15 General 17 Banana 19 Rights 20 Urban 22 Pear 24 Next **SHADED WORD:** RUSTLE

MISSING LINK from page 115

ACROSS: 1 Past 3 Thought 9 Looking 10 Chair 11 Title 13 Hydro 14 Stem 16 Nails 18 Warm 19 Tails 21 Poker 23 Ghost 24 Manager 25 Betting 26 News **DOWN:** 1 Polish 2 Shoulder 4 Hog 5 Uncle 6 Heap 7 Piston 8 Dream 12 Thick 15 Triangle 17 String 18 Weigh 20 Storms 21 Petit 22 Hole 24 Men **SHADED WORD:** GEYSER

SUDOKU From Page 105

5	2	8	9	4	3	6	1	7
7	9	3	2	6	1	8	5	4
1	6	4	8	7	5	2	9	3
2	4	1	3	5	9	7	6	8
3	5	6	7	1	8	4	2	9
8	7	9	6	2	4	5	3	1
4	3	7	5	9	6	1	8	2
9	1	5	4	8	2	3	7	6
6	8	2	1	3	7	9	4	5

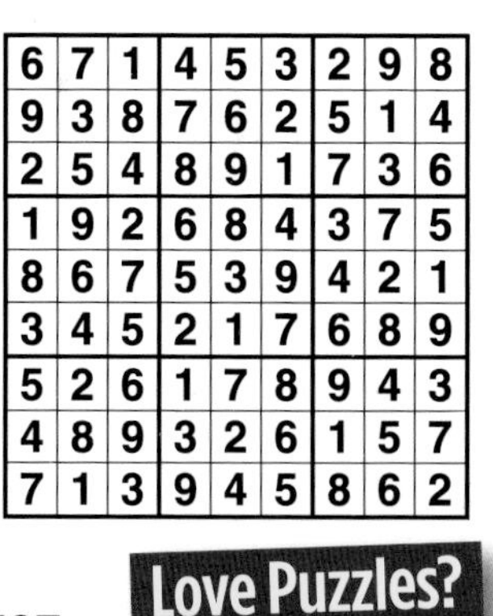

6	7	1	4	5	3	2	9	8
9	3	8	7	6	2	5	1	4
2	5	4	8	9	1	7	3	6
1	9	2	6	8	4	3	7	5
8	6	7	5	3	9	4	2	1
3	4	5	2	1	7	6	8	9
5	2	6	1	7	8	9	4	3
4	8	9	3	2	6	1	5	7
7	1	3	9	4	5	8	6	2

WORD WHEEL from page 105

The nine-letter word is DECONGEST

Thief Of Bethlehem

The small and seemingly insignificant moments in life often turn out to be the most important turning points...

By Valerie Bowes

ather snapped his fingers. I tipped the few miserable coins into his palm and scuttled back out of range.

"Is this it, then? Bethlehem's bulging at the seams with people here to pay this tax, and this is all you can come up with?"

"Most of them are as poor as us," I muttered sullenly. "Nothing worth stealing in the first place and the tax-collector's had what little there was."

He raised his face and his fists heavenwards, careful to keep the money caged tightly in his fingers.

"Why couldn't me and Naomi have had sons – many sons – instead of one useless daughter?"

I'd heard the whine so often I could usually ignore it, but this time it grated me raw.

"Sons!" I said, bitterness twisting my mouth. "And they'd have cooked and cleaned for you like I've done ever since my mother died, would they? And never minded you blowing all they earned on wine and gambling at El-Ibrahim's every night? And kept you fed and put you to bed when you were so drunk you didn't know which way up you were?"

He raised his hand and I pressed my spine into the wall to get as far away from him as I could. A few flakes of dried mud crumbled from the wall and fell down to join the others on the floor.

"Don't you speak back to me like that, girl. I'm your father."

Some father, I thought, resentment rising sourly in my throat. *All he wants is to drink and gamble his life away, and if the only way he could get the money was for me to sell myself on the streets, he'd bear the shame bravely.*

He turned away and I made haste to set his meal on the rickety table.

"I hear the inn on the Nazareth road is looking for help," he said, tearing a hunk from the bread and spitting an olive pip on the floor. "Get yourself down there first thing tomorrow morning, and don't come back until you've got some decent money."

"The inn on the Nazareth road is looking for help – go earn us some money"

Continued overleaf...

The newborn baby caused quite a stir in town

Continued from previous page

The landlord's wife was a good woman but she was rushed off her plump feet and consequently short-tempered.

"Rebekkah, isn't it? Well, make yourself useful and I'll see you at least get some food to take back to that feckless father of yours."

She turned her head as one of the inn servants staggered past with a clinking pile of dirty dishes.

"Careful! You drop any of those and I'll have your guts. I haven't got enough to go round as it is." She waved her hand irritably. "We're stuffed to the rafters. Never known so many folk to be crammed into the town. We've even got a couple in the stable. Two about to become three, unless I'm much mistaken. Which I'm not. You can't tell me anything about babies. Had seven of my own. Don't just stand there, girl. Get on with it."

She was even shorter-tempered when I went back to the inn the next morning.

"Been up all night with the girl in the stable. Nice, healthy boy and little trouble to speak of, even though it's her first, she tells me. But just as I'm getting her settled down and him swaddled, old Jonah and his lads turn up, babbling of angels and making the place stink of sheep. Just what she needed, poor thing. Tell me why a bunch of grown men would come running all the way down from the hills just to see a baby? Never heard the like."

I shook my head sycophantically, but I remembered my star-cast shadow as I ran home with the basket of left-over meats. The night had burned with icy fire. One star in particular had glowed with such diamond sharpness that it lit even the dark alley.

If the shepherds had had a drop or three to drink, to keep out the cold while they watched over the flock, I wasn't surprised if they'd thought angels were dancing in the wine.

The baby's father was a carpenter. The landlord got his money's worth out of him for the next couple of weeks, making and mending while Bethlehem gradually emptied as the tax-payers trudged, grumbling, back to their own homes.

The strangers came at noon on the fourteenth day; an old man with the opaque pupils of blindness, a Nubian with skin like polished ebony and a man with a strange, flat face and slanting eyes.

To say they caused a stir would be putting it mildly. The spitting camels and fractious mules took up every inch of the meagre courtyard and the attendants pushed the rest of us out of their masters' way with lordly indifference.

I didn't mind. Nobody ever considered my comfort anyway, and there were rich pickings for me. With everyone's attention firmly fixed, my nimble fingers were able to snaffle a good haul. It wouldn't be long before I was told my help was no longer required here, so I was desperate to squirrel away everything I could to stave off my father's heavy hand in the coming days.

The strangers paid no mind to the staring folk, but after questioning the landlord in a mixture of languages, they took some things from their packs and went into the stable. When they came out again, they were empty-handed. My curiosity was aroused.

Later that evening, I took my chance. The man was working in the inn; I could

hear the rhythmic drag of his saw and the drone of the landlord's voice. I hoped the woman would be asleep after all the excitement of the day, but I'd think up some plausible reason to be there if it turned out that she wasn't.

The click of the latch sounded loud in my ears, but the girl curled in the piled hay didn't stir. I crept closer. She was so young. Only a little older than me, I guessed, seeing the roundness of the pale face and the bitten nails.

The skin around her eyes looked bruised with tiredness. I wasn't surprised. I wouldn't have liked to jiggle all the way from Nazareth perched on the rump of a donkey, nine months pregnant and as big as a mountain.

Then she'd had all the hard work to birth the baby and I thought, with an unaccustomed flash of compassion, that having Jonah and the boys peering at her immediately afterwards wouldn't have been exactly welcome.

At least she had a man to love her. He was clearly quite a bit older, but I could see he treated her with a sort of reverence. And now she had a son. She would never know the pain of being unloved, as I did.

I clenched my hand and banished any stray scruples to the back of my mind. Even though the man's tunic bore several neat patches, and her sandals had been repaired more than once, I wouldn't feel bad about stealing anything here. She had so much more than me, after all.

Their bundle was half done up, as though they would be leaving shortly. I slid my fingers inside.

The angular lines of a box met my groping hand. I wriggled it out. The box itself would be worth many shekels, I reckoned as I ran my thumb over the hard silky smoothness of the wood. I slid my nail under the lid and pushed it open. It was full of a greasy substance like solid milk.

I banished any stray scruples and slid my fingers inside their bundle

I'd never seen it before, but the smell told me what it was, and I nearly dropped it in my amazement. Frankincense!

Weight for weight more valuable than gold. I closed both the lid and my gaping mouth and thrust the box into the neck of my tunic. It lay against my bumping heart; riches enough to keep me safe forever.

With greedy haste, I rummaged in the pack again. This time, I felt a hard lump between my fingers. I drew it out and unwrapped the cloth that covered it.

Dark, dark amber, streaked with white, it felt like a pebble. I raised it to my nose and sniffed, recoiling from the bitter scent. Why on earth would anyone want to give myrrh to a baby? Myrrh was for the dead, not for the newborn. But I knew

Continued overleaf...

Continued from previous page

its value and my heart redoubled its crazy beating.

Surely, this was enough? I could take these precious things and run. Run, and never go back to beatings and humiliation and not enough to eat.

I'd taken the first step, but then I remembered. There were *three* strangers.

Scarcely breathing, I felt among the clothes and small needful things of travel, and I pulled out a gold coin.

I held it to the lantern. A rose noble. I'd never seen one before. It was so beautiful, I could have worn out my eyes just looking at it. I checked swiftly. The girl still slept, but the baby was watching me.

"I need it more than you do," I whispered defiantly, turning my back on the baby's penetrating gaze.

The gold seemed cool and soothing against my work-worn hand. It would keep us for an entire year. My father couldn't say I was a useless daughter when he saw this, could he?

I don't know how long I stood there, wrapped in my dream before reality crowded in on me like the stink in the alleys where I spent my days.

The coin was no use to me. No shopkeeper would take it for a chicken or some olives and give a bucketful of small coin as change.

The same with the costly perfumes. I was on first name terms with every fence in the town, but they would give me less than a hundredth of its worth, if they didn't kill me for it – and who would care for my father then?

I could give him the incense to sell.

The fences would cheat him worse than they would cheat me. I knew what was what, but he didn't. Though even with the pittance they'd give him, we could move away from Bethlehem, to some place that didn't know us, and start afresh.

He'd gamble it away in a matter of months, of course. We'd be back where we started but it would make him happy for a while and I could keep the coin, safe and secret, just to enjoy its beauty.

Maybe it would even buy me a husband eventually.

I clenched my hand on its richness while my delusion crumbled and faded. Skinny, scruffy Rebekkah, with the useless father. Who'd want me, even with a gold noble as my dowry?

I felt a strange tingle in the middle of my shoulderblades and jerked my head around sharply.

The baby was still looking at me. He was so small, so vulnerable, but there was something in his gaze that made me feel as if he was looking deep inside me, to

The baby's gaze made me feel as if he was looking deep inside, to the real me

the real Rebekkah who was hiding within. The one nobody knew about but me.

The one who wasn't a thief.

I looked again, longingly, at the noble, felt the lump that was the precious ointment as it lay under my tunic. Then I lugged it out and stuffed it back into the depths of the bundle, the coin tucked securely in beside it.

"It's yours, kid. Consider it a gift."

I thought I saw him smile, but it was probably wind. He was too young for smiling, wasn't he?

I didn't feel much like smiling myself, as I slipped out of the stable. I felt more like crying, to be honest.

But underneath the nagging doubt that I had turned down the best opportunity I'd ever get, there was something that made me stand taller.

"Have they gone?"

The voice made me jump.

"Who's that?"

"It's only me – Ezra."

Someone moved from the shadows of the yard into the light from the inn window and I saw it was one of Jonah's boys. The tall one with the curly hair, only a couple of years older than I was. He came closer, looking down at me. I could smell sheep on his rough tunic but, somehow, it didn't matter much. Perhaps it was because the scent of incense was still in my nose.

"Do you mean them?" I jerked my head at the stable door.

He nodded.

"We came to see the baby earlier," he mumbled. "I just wanted…"

His shoulders sagged a little, as though he didn't really know what it was he wanted. If he hadn't been a shepherd, I'd have called him sheepish.

"She's asleep, but the baby isn't. If you're quiet, I'm sure she won't mind."

I opened the door. The girl had woken. She was sitting up, the baby in her arms, and she smiled at us as we went in.

"Um, this is Ezra, a shepherd," I said. Spinning a line at a moment's notice was as natural as breathing to me. "He just came to see how you were, before he goes back to the flock."

I nudged him in the ribs. He moved forward awkwardly, making the same soothing noises to the baby as he would to a lamb. I went back to the inn yard and sat on a sack of hay.

When he came out, it was as if he was clothed in a lingering solemnity, but he came to sit beside me as if it was the most natural thing in the world. He pulled some bread from the pouch at his belt and we ate it, huddled together under his cloak.

When I left, he made me promise to meet him the next time they came back into town, and the look in his eyes told me I wouldn't need to buy myself a husband with stolen goods.

One day, I would have a man of my own to love me. And maybe a beautiful, precious son, like the girl in the stable.

My boy would be a shepherd like his father, and one thing I knew for sure; his mother wouldn't be a thief.

"To us, the Wise Men's gifts of gold, frankincense and myrrh becomes blurred with repetition, but supposing you had these precious things within your grasp…"

Italian Interlude

Coffee, family tradition and the secret of enduring love – my wise old friend Ignatio shared them all with me

By Ali Anderson

Casa Conduta – the shop looked as if it had been in the slender old man's family for generations, never changing much, just adding a couple more items that might be desirable to tourists as the decades went on. He stood there at the doorway of the dark shop front, smoking his cigarette and watching the world go by. Lulled by his calm stance, for once I stepped back to sit and survey as well.

The square was bustling at lunch. There were the tourists seated outside the cafe, like me talking advantage of the three-course lunch for nine Euros fifty, including wine and coffee. The local men sat outside the bar, taking their short, black coffees and watching too, as they stopped to break before eating. Everything was bustling, yet there was calm. Calm in a way that meant I could make this lunch last me three hours and nobody would hustle me out, despite the queue of Brits waiting for a table.

My fish soup arrived and I savoured its taste and warmth, looking over again to Casa Conduta and the slim, elderly man who was now putting out the cigarette and performing what must surely be a daily routine of taking in the assorted fishing rods, spades, T-shirts and souvenirs before closing up for the long lunch hour.

The shop looked quite different inside. There were linen tablecloths, dresses a local matron might buy and lace runners ideal for antique mahogany sideboards. It looked cool and deliciously inviting as I gazed over the square to the dark interior. I would go in later, investigate. But there was all the time in the world, I thought. No rush at all. The local red wine was rough and warming, and the seafood rice arriving at my little table was all I could have wanted at that moment.

I could make this lunch last for three hours and nobody would hustle me out

Mr Casa Conduta locked the dark doors of his emporium and walked five yards to the similar wrought iron and oak doors beside the bar – the local equivalent of a tenement, I guessed. He

Continued overleaf...

ILLUSTRATIONS: MANDY DIXON, THINKSTOCK

There was peace here

Continued from previous page

unlocked them and disappeared – I imagined, to some cool marble and mahogany dining room to eat then snooze in a darkened, shuttered room until the heat of the day was past its peak and he could return.

Every day I dodged the buffet lunch after the conference and wandered along to the old town square to sit in the cafe. I had become strangely obsessed with the traditional old shop and its weird array of products for sale. I walked back to the hotel to nap after lunch, then took an early evening stroll to the square and perused the tablecloths and linens in Ignatio's store.

He had introduced himself as I purchased an embroidered Easter tablecloth. "I am Ignatio Conduta," he said, offering his hand then pointing to the festive Christmas cloths with their red stitching. "You like…?"

Christmas seemed so far away on this island of eternal sunshine, and it was something I'd been avoiding thinking about. Like going home at the weekend, it was something I'd deal with later. My daily routine of lunch in the square and a meander around Casa Conduta was oddly comforting. I'd rather live on like this, with no more to worry about than arriving in time to eat outside, than dwell on Christmas and all its complications.

On the third day of my little post-lunch ritual he offered me coffee. The square was quieter in the early evening, after the five pm rush of traffic and honking of horns had passed. There was something strangely intimate about the process of him preparing the little metal pot, spooning in the grains then filling it with water before placing on the cooker top and lighting the gas. It seemed so long since I'd had a father or any older relative to talk to, the confidences came easily in the dim shop interior.

"My husband was married before," I told him. "He has a daughter. She hates me. She's ten and blames me for her parents' break-up. But that was years ago, long before I came on the scene. She wants their time together to be just her and him. I don't mind, but we've hardly been married five minutes, and it's exhausting, always trying not to offend her. My *existence* offends her, you know…"

The old man nodded, as though he did know, and poured me more coffee.

"There's so much bad feeling, you see. How can I bring a little baby into that?"

"My husband and I want to have a family of our own, but I'm scared that there won't be a place for another child in this whole set-up. There's so much bad feeling, you see. How can I bring a little baby into that? We had such a beautiful wedding, but now my whole life feels as if it's been consumed by access arrangements and jealousies. It's all just so petty…"

Ignatio nodded wisely and although he didn't say much, the cool, comforting little store was like a confessional, where I could voice all my innermost feelings and never even feel guilty.

"Tomorrow," he said as I prepared to stroll back to the confines of the five-star conference centre, taking my mind back to hotel developments and tourist strategies. If I could keep one little vestige of the calm of Casa Conduta with me, pack it up and take it home at the weekend, I'd be OK.

"Tomorrow," I agreed, smiling as I took a glance back at the old man waving as I left the square.

He had the coffee warming every day after that. The smell as I entered his domain was warm and rich and welcoming. I always managed to find another item or two to purchase, as well.

On the fifth day, he pointed to the stern woman in the photo frame in the back shop.

"That's my Magdelena." He laughed. "Oh, she could give me a hard time, that one. She'd scold me for saying it, but she had got a bit, how you put it, plump there. She was very beautiful, when she was a young woman. It was hard for her to get older, put on the fat, as you say it..."

Then there was a sparkle, the hint of a tear in his dark eyes.

"When did she die?" I asked gently.

"Last year," he told me. "That's the last photo I took. She'd kill me if she knew I put it up, but I miss her stern, scolding face the most..."

"Rob – that's my husband," I told my new friend, "sometimes treats me like a baby. When I get upset about stuff he talks about everything so sensibly and it annoys me."

"Magdelena, she made me crazy for years." Ignatio smiled fondly. "Now there's nobody to scold me.

"She had a son when we met. She was widow, you know. My son, Enrico, he was a wild boy. Always causing bother at the school. He made the teacher grey!" He raised his eyebrows and his eyes twinkled with mirth.

"How did you cope?" I asked. "Didn't it come between you?"

"We argued about it, my wife and I, many times," he explained. "But if you love the woman, you love the child and you never go back on it. Never, ever. You sign up for it; is done."

He made it sound quite simple.

"My mother-in-law, she hated me." He raised his eyebrows. "I get Magdelena pregnant, you see. Big scandal when her mother think she should still be wearing widow's black, five years after the first husband die. She want to pay me to go away and have the baby adopted. Then, when she saw my baby Rosaria, everything change, you know. Magdelena and I, we were married for fifty-four years. Loads of loving, plenty shouting, but we sign up for it. I'd go back, do it all again tomorrow. My mother-in-law, she's nearly one hundred and lives by herself, along the seafront." He nodded towards the fisherman's cottages along by the shore. "She still thinks I'm not good enough, but I'm her Magdelena's husband. Father to Enrico, Rosaria, little Ignatio and Livia, grandfather to all their children. It's done.

Continued overleaf...

Continued from previous page

We signed up for it, made it work…"

He gave me faith, Ignatio; made everything seem certain in what was such an unsure set-up. We signed up for it, and there was loads of love, if a bit of shouting. It was done.

On day six he gave me a parcel, and a card. "You open later," he said.

He was closing up that Friday night for Christmas. "I finish up tonight," he explained. "Rosaria picks up me and Nonna. We drive to the mountains. We have a house there we visit for holidays. Very cold! I need the jumpers…" He gestured at the few hooded sweatshirts that hung on a rail in the darkest alcove of Casa Conduta. I couldn't imagine that it would be as cold in the mountains as it would be in London when I descended.

"I'll take one of those as well, please," I decided. "It's the least I can do after all your coffee and kindness."

"On the house," he twinkled and suddenly I could see the young man Magdelena had loved and scolded for all these years.

I slipped on the warm, fleecy sweatshirt as the plane gained altitude and the air temperature cooled. Sipping my airline coffee, which wasn't a patch on Ignatio's, I opened the parcel. It was the Christmas tablecloth, festively embroidered with its red and green stitching.

Merry Christmas, my young friend Laura, read the inscription. *Use this to make a Christmas tradition with your family.*

There was snow on the ground as we landed at Heathrow and suddenly it seemed real that tomorrow was Christmas Eve. Rob's face was anxious as he waited at the barrier; I could see the worry through his smiles and chat. He knew we were in a sticky place when I'd been sent on the last-minute training seminar. His arms felt warm and reassuring as we headed to the car park.

"Hannah's still being a bit difficult about when she's coming over Christmas," he confided as we got in the car. "She says her mother doesn't know what she's doing yet."

My husband glanced at me, no doubt waiting for my usual terse response. And that's when I realised that this was love – not just the hearts and flowers or the lovely wedding, but the moving on through the hard stuff and getting closer all the way. We signed up for it and it was done – we would make it work over years and years, and this was just the start.

"Well, she can come any time she likes." I smiled at the man I loved so much; even more than on that glorious wedding day. "I've got us a Christmas tablecloth and I'm planning on doing a lot of cooking…"

THE AUTHOR SAYS…

"In a sunny square on holiday, I watched an elderly man closing up his shop for lunch. I found myself imagining what his life was like."